TOP TIP

Practical problem-solving is the approach of this book, with sections on understanding your toddler's behaviour and ways of tackling new challenges.

Welcome
to Ready Steady Toddler!

* A great read for all parents about to experience the big changes that your child will go through as they leave the baby stage behind and become a boisterous and inquisitive toddler.

* We have split the book into four sections covering your tot's development, troubleshooting specific areas like tantrums, food or bedtime, health and safety, and sources of further help.

* You'll find easy-to-digest guidance from our experts, tips on devising helpful routines and keeping your patience, handy checklists, wise words from seasoned parents and more.

* Sure Start health visitor
MARGARET DUNCAN

* Consultant paediatrician
ZOË DUNHILL

* Child psychologist
CHRISTINE PUCKERING

Meet our panel of experts

Our team of Scottish experts have been invaluable in the preparation of this publication.

They've heard it all before from other parents. We hope that this book will confirm that many of you are doing the right thing!

contents

you & your child 1

4   **Keep it positive** Encouraging happy toddlers

6   **Looking after number one** Your own wellbeing counts

8   **Other people** Tips on choosing childcare

10   **Playing it right** The how, the what and the where

14   **Who's a little chatterbox?** From the magic first word to talking the talk

16   **Tune in, turn off** Measurements and milestones

17   **Get talking** Understanding and communicating with each other

18   **How am I doing?** Development and new skills

20   **Look at me, mum!** They've come a long way, but they still need you

22   **Families** They come in all shapes and sizes

parenting issues 2

24   **Getting to know you** Understanding your toddler

26   **Say what you mean** Structures and boundaries

28   **Temper temper** Rise above the tantrums and stay sane

32   **Feed 'em well** Healthy eating and high-chair harmony

38   **Toilet training** Don't let it drive you potty

40   **Silent nights** Banish power struggles with bedtime routines

43   **New arrival** Smoothing the ruffles

health & safety 3

46   **Head to toe** Essential maintenance

48   **'I don't feel well'** Getting through those poorly times

51   **Special delivery** Help for specialised needs

52   **Safety first** A safe home for boisterous bodies

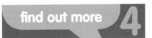
find out more 4

54   **You and your health service** Don't struggle on alone

55   **Find out more** An A-Z of useful organisations

The toddler years are when your child develops from a dependent baby into a person in their own right. It can be a confusing time for you both. Learning to see things from your child's point of view will help. This first section looks at the changes you can expect and gives tips on how to enjoy this challenging stage.

*you & your child
...a positive partnership

WHAT YOU CAN FIND IN THIS SECTION

| POSITIVE PARENTING | IT STARTS WITH YOU | OTHER PEOPLE | PLAYTIME | MIND YOUR LANGUAGE | MILESTONES |

Keep it positive

The secret to having happy kids is to love them no matter what. Praise them as much as you can as they learn to be more independent and express their feelings.

The time between your toddler's first and third birthdays can be the most fascinating of your life – and theirs. It can also be the most demanding! So it helps to take a practical, 'positive parenting' approach to the many challenges you'll face as your child grows up.

EXPERIENCED PARENTS OLD HAND Experienced mums have found it helpful to put their children's feelings into words before they have the ability to explain things for themselves.

NEW HAND First-time mums worry that when they first ignore a behaviour it gets worse. Good sign! Your child wants your attention, so stick to your plan. **FIRST-TIME PARENTS**

6 key ways to encourage happy toddlers

* Praise them, to encourage them to behave well.

* Respect your children as individuals with their own personalities, thoughts, needs and wishes. This does not mean giving into them over everything but recognising when they're feeling unhappy or angry.

* Set out simple rules and make it clear you expect them to be followed.

* Ensure everyone in the family follows the same rules.

* Always be consistent.

* Avoid giving harsh punishments like smacking or excessive shouting.

GETTING AN ACTION PLAN

See the world through their eyes The world is an exciting place to your toddler, but it can also be confusing. The way they see things depends on their personality as well as on how far their brains have developed. You can help by making a real effort to see things from your child's point of view as they get used to being more independent. You'll find more information and tips on pages 18–21.

Lead the way Kids learn by copying so show them love and affection, treat them – and others – with consideration, listen to their views and respect their feelings. And remember it's no good telling them that hitting or shouting is not allowed if that's what you do.

Lay down some ground rules Children naturally want to please you but they need to know what you expect of them. So set clear, simple rules that they can understand. See pages 26–27 for more hints.

Think of their feelings When your toddler misbehaves it's often because they don't know any other way to deal with their feelings. You can help by letting them know that they're allowed to show their emotions, and by giving them a name for their feelings so that they can express them. For example say, 'It looks to me as if you're upset/happy/sad/cross/frustrated.' Don't worry if you haven't identified it correctly; they'll soon put you right if need be.

Tell them when you're pleased Your toddler wants your attention more than anything else. When you praise what they do, they'll respond by doing it again and again. Explain what you mean. Say, 'Thank you for putting your blocks away' or, 'I can see you're really taking time over that painting', rather than just a general 'That's a good boy/girl'.

Ignore minor naughtiness Just as rewarding good behaviour with attention is the best way to get kids to repeat it, ignoring things that you don't want them to do can be a good way of stopping them. Any kind of attention – even a telling-off – can prolong bad habits and behaviour. Don't overreact. Learn to turn a blind eye to minor sillinesses.

It's not them, it's what they do Constant criticism creates bad feeling and it can lead to even more difficult behaviour, not less. Emphasise that it's your child's behaviour you're unhappy about, not them. For example, say, 'It's upsetting when you hit your brother,' rather than, 'You're bad/spoilt.'

Avoid harsh punishments Smacking, shouting and swearing is never the way to get the best out of your child. It makes them angry and resentful, which can result in more tantrums and bad behaviour. Plus, it can also make your child scared of you. It can show them that the answer to strong feelings is to lash out – not a good message. And a bad atmosphere will make you feel stressed.

Focus on solutions Seeing tantrums, potty training, sleep and mealtimes as problems can make them seem impossible to solve. But by focusing on finding answers you can feel confident and more in control. The same goes for your tot; help them to put things right if they've behaved badly. For instance, say something like, 'You hit Ross and now he's upset. How can we sort it out?'

Stay in touch with your feelings Being a parent can be a tough job and no one gets it right all the time. It helps to say sorry if you feel you've handled something badly. It shows you're human and teaches children how to apologise. If you feel you're on the brink of losing control, take yourself away from the situation for a while to calm down. Above all, count your successes. You're doing a great job!

It's not your fault! All parents sometimes feel as if they've reached the end of their tether. But what you see as 'naughtiness' is part and parcel of your tot's urge to explore the world. It is wearing but they need your love and support as much as ever.

POSITIVE PARENTING: WHAT IT MEANS TO ME

'It means adopting practical strategies and techniques that shape your child's behaviour in a positive way.'
Lynsey Kemlo, mum

'Positive parenting means feeling good about yourself as a parent, setting realistic limits and letting your child know that he or she is loved and that you really enjoy his or her company.'
Christine Puckering, child psychologist

'Setting a good example at all times, providing security and warmth, focusing on and rewarding good behaviour and letting them know how much you love them.'
Alison Rennie, paediatrician and mum

TOPTIP
Get down to your child's level and make eye contact when you talk, especially when you have something important to say to them.

Looking after number one

Your own health and happiness are very important ingredients in raising contented and confident kids. We show you how to look after number one by putting yourself first sometimes.

Like all parents, you want to do the best for your child, to provide them with love and all the things they need to grow and develop. But how do you juggle the demands of looking after a toddler with your family, friends, partner, work and leisure? The good news is, you don't have to spend a fortune on toys and games. Nor do you need any special skills. What your child needs most of all is *you*.

Toddler battles are most likely when you feel under valued, over-worked or that life's getting on top of you.

So you have to learn to put yourself first sometimes. Try these useful tips:

Choose one thing you'd like to do for yourself over the next week and make time to do it. It could be a trip to the cinema, a drink with a friend, getting stuck into a good book or having a relaxing soak in a warm bath.

Take a look at your lifestyle How healthy is your diet? When did you last take any exercise? Are you getting enough good sleep? Think about how to make changes.

Learn to switch off, even for a few minutes Listen to some music, read a magazine, catch up with an episode of your favourite TV programme or do some exercise.

TOP TIP

Two heads are better than one. If things get on top of you, have a brainstorming session with your partner, friend, mum or sister, and look for mother and toddler groups where problems can be shared.

you say

'I can't afford a babysitter, so I got together with some other mums in my area to form a babysitting circle. We use 'tokens' to pay each other. I use the time to go for a swim.'
Marie, 23, mum to Lucy, eight months and Kate, 20 months

'When Mike comes in from work I make a cup of tea and we take ten minutes to talk about our day.'
Maxine, 25, mum to Hope, 13 months and Jasper, three'

'My mum told me to learn to live with a bit of mess. It doesn't matter if the house is a bit untidy. It was the best advice I ever had.'
Claire, 34, mum to Ali, nine months, Jake, two, and Lee, five

THINK POSITIVELY!

You may think your own feelings have nothing to do with your child's behaviour. But if you constantly think, 'I'm a rubbish mum/dad', this can lead to the thought, 'I can't control my toddler', which in turn can make you feel anxious or depressed. Your feelings can cause you to shout, smack or weep if your tot misbehaves. The message your child gets is, 'My feelings are so strong, even my mum can't cope. I must be very bad.' This can cause insecurity and lead to further misbehaviour. But things are often not as bad as they seem. Try replacing negative thoughts with more positive – realistic – ones.

IF YOU THINK…	TRY THINKING…
 I'm totally drained looking after my kids. I'll never ever have any energy.	Looking after children is hard work, but if I look after myself, eat properly and make time to relax, I'll feel less tired. As my kids get older I'll have more energy. 
My toddler is just never going to sleep through the night.	My toddler doesn't sleep through the night now, but there are things I could try that will help. I'll give them a go.
My toddler always has a tantrum when we go to the supermarket.	It's normal for toddlers to have tantrums because they're becoming more independent. I'll think about what triggers the tantrum and what I can do to avoid it next time we're at the shops.
Oh no, my toddler wet the bed again last night. He's never going to be toilet trained.	All toddlers have the odd accident when they're toilet training. I'll put a waterproof cover between the sheet and the mattress then it won't matter so much.
My kids hate each other – they're always fighting and screaming.	My kids sometimes don't get on but all brothers and sisters quarrel from time to time. I'll try ignoring the less serious scraps.

Make home child-friendly Move any breakable and valuable things out of reach and make sure surfaces and furniture are easy to clean.

Have some kid-free zones even if it's just a corner of your bedroom.

Just say no Before you take on anything new this week, ask yourself if it will benefit you and your family. If the answer is 'No', don't do it. Don't feel guilty – 'No' is really a 'Yes' to yourself.

Start planning Imagine yourself in six months time. What do you want to be doing? Do just one thing over the next week that will take you closer to your goal. Accept that you don't have to be great at everything, don't be afraid to ask for help and take any help that is offered.

WHEN IT'S MORE THAN JUST A BAD DAY

You should talk to the health visitor or doctor if you're finding every day a struggle, if you feel constantly depressed, anxious or exhausted even when you're getting enough sleep, if you no longer get enjoyment from life and/or if you've ever felt suicidal.

Other people

It may be a wrench to leave your child in someone else's care, but if you choose right, the experience can benefit both of you.

EXPERT FILES *Child psychologist*

'Make rules about things that really matter, and then ensure you stick to those rules you do make. It is also important that other people who spend time with the children use the same rules. If Mum says it's OK, why should Dad or Gran make a fuss? It means the rule is flexible and so the children will try to bend it. It's important to agree the rules with partners and grannies and other carers and then stick to them. Don't undermine each other or the children will undermine you all!'

Christine Puckering, Department of Child and Adolescent Psychiatry, Glasgow University

Young children need security and routine in their lives but you don't have to be the only one who cares for them. You may need to go out to work or you may feel that having time apart will help them learn new skills and also encourage their growing sense of independence.

What do you need? Finding childcare can be difficult and stressful as there are so many different types and some are very costly. They range from child-minders, nurseries and nannies to friends and family. Local authorities can provide information on childcare. Or log on to www.scottishchildcare.gov.uk for childcare information for your area and details of financial support you may be entitled to.

What to look out for When you hand over the care of your child to someone else it's important that emotional, as well as physical, needs are looked after and that your carer is in tune with your views on issues like behaviour, sweets and TV. Before making your choice, take time to discuss these areas in detail to avoid clashes later on.

Toddlers get confused

if there is a very big difference in the way they are looked after at home and elsewhere, which is why it's so important to agree some ground rules with your child's carers. Naturally, there will be minor differences in the way things are done.

Safety first Between ages one and three your tot is an active little explorer, so a major consideration when choosing a carer or a care setting is safety. Registered settings like childminders and nurseries will be well aware of safety issues. But if your child is going to be cared for by a relative or someone who has not had children of their own, their home may not be child friendly and you'll need to work with them

to make sure that it is quite safe.

Your child's needs Because your toddler is developing on so many different fronts, you'll want to look for a carer who can provide them with the right kind of play opportunities and can cater for your child's needs as they change.

Give it time In the first few days you might find that they cry and cling to you when you leave. They might be stand-offish when you return and revert to babyish behaviour for a time. This is your child showing how he or she feels about being separated from you. Be patient and show that you understand their feelings.

ask christine

Q My mum looks after Caitlin two days a week. I've told Mum I don't want her to have sweets, but she insists a few chocolate buttons won't do any harm. What can I do? Mary

A A family member can offer great continuity and familiarity for your child but it does make it harder to address problem areas like this.

First of all let your mum know how much you appreciate her looking after Caitlin and what it means to you both.

Tell her honestly and clearly why it is important to you that she doesn't give sweets and that you no longer want her to do this.

Find out why she wants to give Caitlin sweets – usually it's a sign of affection or a special treat – and agree on something that she could give her instead that you are all happy with.

CHILDCARE CHECKLIST

Useful questions to ask carers:

For individual carers
* How many children do you look after and how much individual attention can you give my child?

* How long have you worked with children? What are your training qualifications?

* What will my tot's daily routine be?

* What food and drink do you provide?

* Can I see where my little one will sleep during the day?

* What will you provide to help mental and physical development?

* Do you go out to play clubs or the park?

* How will you let me know how my child is getting on?

* How would you handle food refusal and potty training?

* How do you handle discipline?

* Are you trained in first aid and what would you do in an emergency?

* Do you have any friends who are likely to visit during the day? (If so, you'll need to meet them too).

For group facilities
* Can I look around and see where my child will be?

* How many kids come here, and how much individual attention will my child get?

* Do you organise regular outings?

* Where is the outside play area?

* Can you offer flexible hours and/or a part-time place?

* When was your last Care Commission inspection and what were the results?

GETTING TO KNOW YOU
Some children cheerfully cope with being away from their parents but others are much more clingy. Careful preparation pays off, so try these tips.

* Don't spring a new care arrangement on them. Talk about it beforehand.

* Visit your chosen care option several times before the first day or, if your care giver will be looking after your tot at your home, get them to work with you for a day or two.

* Find ways to show your little one that you like and trust the new care giver.

* Don't try and slip away without saying anything,

otherwise your child may panic and get upset. Give them a hug and kiss before you go.

* Say a clear 'bye-bye' and tell them when you'll see them again, like 'after lunch' or 'when you've been to the park'.

* Don't be late collecting your child.

* Allow time for settling in. But if your child is still very upset after several weeks, talk it over with members of staff and/or your GP or health visitor.

5 things to consider when choosing childcare

* Your child's age and whether they have any special needs.

* Whether they prefer group or one-to-one situations.

* Work commitments.

* Facilities that are available locally.

* Whether it's affordable.

Playing it right

For toddlers, playing is as important as healthy food and fresh air. It helps them to develop their language skills and, most important of all, it's fun! Join in and help them make the most of it.

TOP TIP
The chances are that you've got loads of things around the house that will be just as fascinating to your toddler as expensive toys.

5 great things about play-time

* Playing is a natural way for kids to learn and develop new skills.

* It helps build their confidence and makes them feel good about themselves.

* It gives them the opportunity to exercise, develop their physical coordination and get rid of any frustrations.

* It's a chance to meet and mix with other kids.

* It creates a bond between you and your child.

For your child, the years up to age three are all about discovering who they are and what they can (and can't) do. Playing and experimenting is how children learn and it also helps them to let off steam.

HELPING YOUR CHILD GET THE MOST OUT OF PLAY

You're your child's best toy. By encouraging play you'll strengthen your relationship with your child. Kids love playing with parents, using them as the doctor or the horse.

Make the time Spend time playing with your child each day, even if it's only a short spell. This gives them a sense of their importance to you and makes for a happy child.

Put yourself in their shoes Playing with your little one is a great way to get

in touch with your inner child! Get down to their level, forget about being a 'grown-up' and let your imagination run free.

Choose the right toys

Different toys appeal to different age groups, and you can have fun choosing the best ones for your child's stage of development. On the right are some playtime ideas to get you started.

Talk about it Playing is one of the key ways in which your tot develops their language skills. When playing, talk to your child and take the opportunity to extend their vocabulary. For example, if your child says, 'It's an aeroplane' you can reply, 'Yes, it's an aeroplane. Shall we see if we can make it fly? Where do you think it's going?' That way they learn words and ideas about what aeroplanes do.

Let them explore Allow your child to play at their own pace. Sometimes just sit quietly with them and notice what they are doing – perhaps say the things you can see such as, 'I can see you have built a big tower there'. Let them take the lead.

Have a play corner Find a space in your home where your little one can play safely and keep it as a safe, dedicated area free

Continued on page 12

HIDDEN TREASURE

Research shows that playthings which use children's senses are especially important in helping them understand how things work. This doesn't mean you need lots of bought toys. Instead, keep a 'treasure basket' of household objects for your child to explore. Change the contents regularly to keep them interested.

It could include fir cones, shells, piece of loofah, wooden bath brush, shoe brush, cotton dishcloth, wooden spoons, different sized paintbrushes, raffia mats, dolly clothes pegs, egg cups, metal or plastic spoons of different sizes, wooden bowls, saucepans and lids, salt and pepper shakers (empty), metal or plastic beakers, tea strainer, sieve, washed food trays, lemon squeezer, tennis ball, bean bag, notepad, big bits of greaseproof paper and tin foil, different sized cardboard boxes, kitchen paper tubes.

SAFETY FIRST Choose items big enough not to be swallowed and avoid sharp edges or points.

WHICH TOY? 12 TO 24 months

Your child is becoming more independent. He or she needs toys that help them practise their new-found capabilities such as walking, talking and fine finger skills. They begin to learn the meaning of words such as 'up' and 'down', 'in' and 'out', 'big' and 'small', and need play things that enable them to explore these.

As they start to feed themselves and are ready for potty training, they also need opportunities for messy play, as well as toys that help them get used to all the new things they're learning to do.

With the huge choice of toys available in the shops, it can be difficult to know which ones to get. Every child is different and develops at their own rate, so be guided by your toddler and their interests.

Toys that help them use their body and gain balance Sit-and-ride animals, push-along bike, brick lorry, tractor, large balls, rolling rattles.

Toys that help them develop fine finger skills and hand/eye coordination Screwing toys, stacking toys, sorting toys, simple jigsaws, threading toys, blocks, put-together train, bucket and spade.

Toys that help them understand different actions Toys with buttons, bells or levers, hammering toys, posting toys, nesting beakers, wind-up items such as a musical box.

Toys that help develop their imagination Dolls, teddies, puppets, playhouse, dressing-up clothes, hats, shoes.

Toys that help to teach about volume, weight and concepts such as floating, sinking, measuring Floating duck, beakers, jugs and other containers, straws, tubes, bubbles.

Toys that let them make a mess Powder paints, large brushes, sugar paper, wallpaper, lining paper, crayons, modelling clay.

Toys to cuddle and comfort Teddy bears, rabbits and lots of other soft, furry animals.

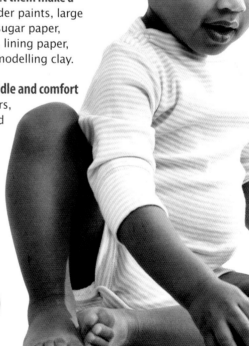

WHICH TOY? 25 TO 36 months

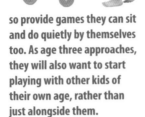

Your child's physical and language skills are becoming more advanced. As well as toys that give them the chance to practise their physical abilities, they need toys that encourage them to widen their vocabulary and opportunities for pretend play to exercise their growing imagination. They are able to concentrate better, so provide games they can sit and do quietly by themselves too. As age three approaches, they will also want to start playing with other kids of their own age, rather than just alongside them.

Toys that encourage them to be physically active
Pedal trike, pedal car, swing, see-saw, slide, bean bags, balls, blow-up toys.

Toys for quiet play
Child-sized table and chair, peg board, counting frame, big Lego blocks, threading beads, blackboard and chalks.

Toys for pretend play
Tea-set, doll's cot, dressing-up clothes, puppets, toy telephone and scaled-down versions of grown-up things such as brushes, workbench and tools, gardening tools.

Creative toys
Whistle, drum or saucepan lid and wooden spoon, finger paints, blunt scissors, humming top. Games and puzzles Picture lotto and picture snap, simple wooden jigsaws.

Continued from page 10

of grown-ups' things and clutter. A corner of the sitting room or bedroom will do nicely. See pages 52–53 for safety tips.

Store toys where your child can see them
Keep toys at toddler eye-level where they are easy to get at. Shelves are better than boxes. Store things like Lego, puzzles and jigsaws in plastic boxes so the bits don't get lost. Other good containers include cheap washing-up bowls, plastic vegetable racks, filing trays or string bags.

Rotate toys to avoid boredom
Toddlers don't have a very long attention span and they soon get tired of the same toys. Fortunately, they also have short memories. Putting a few toys away for a little while and then bringing them out again at a later date can give them a new lease of life.

Give your child the chance to play with other kids
Toddler and play groups, playgrounds, nursery classes and toddler exercise classes give your little one the chance to meet and mix with other children and start learning about relating to people outside the family. Many SureStart schemes offer a range of activities, so if

Top tips for story telling

※ Sit comfortably. Make sure you and your child are warm and cosy.

※ Snuggle up with your tot in a corner of the settee or on a big cushion.

※ Throw yourself into it.

※ Read slowly, put lots of expression into your voice and use gestures, funny faces and voices, and sound effects such as rain falling, cows mooing, cars revving.

※ Involve your child. Encourage them to look at the pictures. Point to objects and characters and get them to say who they think they are.

※ Encourage them if they repeat what you've said or make animal sounds.

there's one in your area check it out.

How many toys?
Your toddler doesn't need lots of bought toys. In fact, too many can be over-whelming. It's better to buy a few

carefully chosen play-things rather than a pile of cheap ones that break easily. Simple toys such as blocks are good value as they can be used in lots of different ways. If you don't have much money, join a toy library, ask friends and relatives to get toys or put some money into a 'toy fund' for birthdays and other special occasions.

Encourage your child to clear up Even from an early age your tot can help you to tidy away after a play session. It can help ease them from one activity to another (for example, from playtime to bedtime) and helps teach tidiness and respect for belongings.

Tell me a story All toddlers adore stories and will enjoy being read to long before they can understand them. They'll enjoy snuggling up close and entering the world of imagination. They may only want to look at pictures and turn pages at first. Reading to them helps develop their speech and language skills and can strengthen their bond with you. It helps develop their imagination and create a positive attitude towards books, which will stand them in good stead for life. Many toddlers will spend ages poring over a book (and don't worry if they don't want to finish the story). Using your local library will keep down the expense.

you say

'I've never been a great reader myself but the sheer joy on Lee's face when I read him a story has inspired me. Now I always read him a story before he goes to bed.' *Sheena, 23, mum to Lee, three*

'When I was expecting Maria I found a book all about the birth of a new baby that I used to read to Clark. He couldn't get enough of it. I'm sure it helped when Maria was born.' *Rachel, 27, mum to Clark, four and Maria, two*

'Like all first-time fathers I was nervous about keeping an energetic toddler entertained when I was on my own with him, but our sessions at the park have been really enjoyable and they mean I get some regular fresh air too.' *Stuart, 31, dad to Ryan, four*

EXPERT FILES *Child psychologist*

'In busy families it is hard to set aside even a short time each day to play, but you can make everyday activities playful. Let them push the vacuum cleaner, give them a duster to polish alongside you, play peek-a-boo under the duvet as you make the beds, let them help to make the sandwiches for lunch, wash up any plastic dishes or set the table. It does take twice as long but they'll love it – and does it really matter if the sandwiches are lop-sided?!'

Christine Puckering, Department of Child and Adolescent Psychiatry, Glasgow University

BE ACTIVE! Physical activity is essential to help keep your child fit and healthy and encourage their heart, bones and muscles to grow strong. Physical games also help young brains to develop. Think of ways to give your child plenty of opportunities to move and exercise and practise their growing ability to walk, run, climb, push and pull. If you have a garden, you may want to install a simple sandpit and/or a swing or climbing frame.

Even if you have outdoor play-space at home, your child will still need trips to a local playground where they can walk and run freely, swing, climb and play in a sandpit or a paddling pool under your watchful eye. Whenever possible, try to join in too. When families go walking or bike riding together, everyone gets fit and has fun at the same time. Look out for family fun days in your area and ask your health visitor about what's on offer in your neighbourhood.

Who's a little chatterbox?

Learning to talk changes everything. From that magic first word to a full conversation, you can help your toddler communicate with the world.

TOP TIP
Don't worry if they make mistakes. Words like 'sheeps' are signs that they're applying rules of language. Simply repeat back the correct form.

Your tot has been learning about sound since before they were born. And during their first year they have been gaining the skills they need to speak. Now it all starts to come together. Some time, usually between the ages of nine and 15 months, they will say their first word. Then they'll start talking in their own time.

True or false?
Here are some myths about how quickly they learn.

* Boys are generally slower than girls. False!

* Second kids are slower than first. False!

* Kids exposed to more than one language at home are slower. False!

* If they're not learning, they're lazy. False!

AROUND 12 TO 18 MONTHS
Your toddler will probably be able to say two or three words. Over the next six months or so they will add to these. They point to objects when asked, wave when someone is leaving and say 'Bye-bye'. At this stage words tend to be all-purpose. 'Cat' or 'dog' may refer to all four-legged animals, while mama' or 'dada' can mean anything from 'Great to see you' to 'I'm tired', 'I'm hungry' or 'Give me a cuddle', depending on how it's said. Simple phrases like 'Want drink' or 'All gone' come out as one word.

HOW YOU CAN HELP
* Keep on talking. Experts say toddlers need to hear a word about 500 times before using it.

* Act it out. Help your tot to make connections between actions and words by talking them through what you are doing. For example, 'Let's put your coat on to go out now. First put one arm in the sleeve. Now let's do the other arm.'

* Remember to speak slowly and clearly. Make your voice slightly higher in order to attract your child's attention.

* Baby talk is OK. At first your little one won't pronounce words properly. They might say 'do' for 'dog' or 'dat' for 'that'. You don't need to correct them. They will begin to say things properly in their own good time.

* Help them add more words to their vocabulary with new experiences – a trip on a bus or train, or a visit to a city farm. Talk to them about what you've seen and done.

* Help convey what they say to other people. If others can't follow what your child is saying, help them out so they gain confidence in talking and that what they say is understood.

AROUND 19 TO 24 MONTHS

By 19 months or so, your little one will usually have at least a few words. They may have a working vocabulary of 50 to 70 words and be able to understand as many as 200. They are learning words at a rate of 10 or more a day and are starting to string words together such as 'More 'tatoes', 'Carry me', 'Don't want to'. By the time they are two, they'll usually be able to form sentences of two or three words and sing simple tunes. Most kids will be able to follow simple instructions such as 'Point to your nose', 'Take your shoes to Daddy', 'Where's your hat?' Your child may be able to identify pictures and point to ones that show actions such as running, jumping or crying. As they develop a stronger sense of who they are, they'll also begin to talk about what they like and dislike. Their favourite word may well be 'no'! They will still tend to refer to themselves and other people by name, rather than talking about 'I' or 'me'. For example, 'Tom throw ball' or 'Daddy get it'.

HOW YOU CAN HELP
✳ Talk about what is happening as you go about everyday activities. For example, 'We're putting the toys in the toy box.

Pass me the blocks, Tom. You can help me put them in the box.'

✳ Help them learn to know and name their feelings. For example, 'You're happy to see Grandad', 'You're angry because it's time to stop playing now'.

✳ Use questions and answers to help them realise that communication goes two ways. If something happens ask them why: 'Why is the cat meowing?' If you're looking at a book together, ask them what's happening in the pictures.

AROUND 25 TO 36 MONTHS

Their vocabulary is now growing fast and by about age three your child may have around 300 words and know the meaning of many more. They can follow a two- or three-part instruction like, 'Get the nappy from the basket and bring it to me'. They are getting the hang of 'I', 'me', 'you' and plurals. By three, most kids can put words together to form simple, complete sentences, such as, 'I go now'. In fact, many kids

can now put together quite complex sentences and carry on a conversation, adapting their tone, speech and language to the person they're talking to. They can say their name, age and sex and know major body parts. Other people should be able to understand most of what they say. Their favourite word is 'why?'.

HOW YOU CAN HELP
✳ Join in their make-believe games. Ask what they're doing, where they're going, where they live and what they like to eat.

✳ Encourage them to use words to describe things – the red ball, the soft blanket.

✳ Use every opportunity you can to talk to them.

✳ When looking at a book or TV, encourage them to tell you what's happening and explain why they think things happen.

✳ Encourage them to help you and put names to things. Teach them that different activities have different words. For example, in cooking the words are chop, mix, beat, peel, hot.

✳ Enjoy stories, nursery rhymes and songs together.

Tune in, turn off

There are some great children's TV programmes these days – but don't let the box take over.

5 ways to help your tot get the most out of watching TV

✳ **Help them understand what's on screen.** Explain anything that could prove difficult and encourage them to be an active viewer by asking questions. 'What do you think is going to happen next?' 'Why do you think so-and-so did that?' 'What was your favourite part of the story?'

✳ **Expand on their viewing.** Give your child the chance to take things further by encouraging them in games based on what they have seen. Provide props such as a tea towel for a cloak or make a cardboard crown.

✳ **Don't have the TV on at mealtimes** and keep it out of the bedroom.

✳ **Don't use television to reward or punish.**

✳ **Don't allow TV to be a constant presence in the corner.** Turn it off when you're not watching and play instead.

We all need time to relax and be entertained and that goes for kids too. Television can entertain, inspire, give your child a chance to be quiet – and give you a bit of a break from non-stop activity. But just as a diet of nothing but junk food is bad, large doses of poor quality TV can lead to weight problems and prevent children giving their full attention to more important things, like learning to talk.

The best way for your little one to watch the box is with you – and in small doses. TV can provide opportunities for language development, and can inspire their imagination and start some great games but it shouldn't be used as a childminder, nor to send your child off to sleep.

There are some really good programmes out there, so choose what your child's going to watch (with your tot's help, once they're able to show a preference) and, if possible, sit down together to watch it. When it's over, switch off the TV. However 'educational' a children's programme is – and many are very useful –

television is not the same as interaction with you by talking and looking at books or pictures together. As your child gets older, you'll need to be firm about viewing times. And when you do switch on the TV, follow the five useful hints on the left.

EXPERT FILES *Child psychologist*

'Children learn to talk because someone listens to them and replies. Try turning off the TV and the radio sometimes and look at some pictures together. Catalogues and magazines are fine. Name what they can see, make animal noises and imitate what they say or do. Children's libraries are full of colourful picture books and are very friendly places for children these days. They're even free!'

Christine Puckering, Department of Child and Adolescent Psychiatry, Glasgow University

how to Get talking!

Solving a tricky problem together gets Paul and Charlie talking to each other.

Here's what happens... and what they say.

1 Paul is reading the newspaper and Charlie is on the floor trying to put pieces of Duplo together.

2 Charlie looks up at his father hopefully but Paul is still busy reading.

3 As a cross Charlie throws Duplo bits across the room, Paul puts aside the paper and joins Charlie on the floor.

4 Talking at eye level, Paul shows that he understands his son's frustration as he sets about helping.

5 As well as giving practical help, Paul encourages Charlie to explain what he's trying to do.

'D-a-a-d, can't do it.'

DAD 'I can see you're having a bit of a problem with that.'

'Can't do it.'

DAD 'That looks really frustrating. Would you like some help?'

'What is it you need Charlie?'

'Hold it Dad.'

DAD 'OK! Let's have another go at that, shall we?'

'What were you doing?'

'Make wocket.'

DAD 'You're making a rocket, eh? And what kind of rocket is it?'

'Big blue wocket.'

DAD 'I see. Dad will hold this bit. Now you put that one on top.'

'Well done. Let's make it fly shall we?'

'Z-o-o-o-m'

THINGS TO THINK ABOUT

* How well do you think Paul responded to Charlie's frustration?
* What did Paul say and do to help Charlie develop his speech?
* Is there anything else he could have said or done to help stretch Charlie's language skills?

Remember

* Conversation involves taking turns. Simple question and answer conversations, as well as games like peep-bo, will help your tot get the idea.

* Show your tot you understand what they're trying to tell you by expanding on what they say. It will help them talk more confidently. In the exchange between Paul and Charlie, Paul asks, 'What kind of rocket?' and 'Shall we make it fly?'

* Help your child become aware of their emotions by recognising and naming the feelings they try to express. In our story, Paul says, 'That looks really frustrating.'

* Don't correct your child when words come out wrong but use the correct pronunciation yourself. When Charlie says 'Wocket' his dad repeats back, 'A rocket.'

* Let your tot see your face and come down to their level so they can see what you're talking about by following where you look.

* Toddlers have short memories, so try and keep what you say short and simple.

Each child learns to talk in their own time. But delay in language development can be a sign of hearing or other difficulties. If you suspect a problem, talk to your health visitor. There's probably nothing to worry about but if there is, the sooner you get it diagnosed the better.

How am I doing?

Toddlers learn a lot of exciting new skills in a short time, so tune into your child's needs and let them set the pace.

Alongside the physical skills your child is developing, they're also learning how to use their mind to think, remember, imagine, solve problems and to process the constant stream of information they get from their eyes, ears, nose, hands and mouth. They are learning to make sense of their own and other people's emotions, a skill vital for forming relationships inside and outside the family. Most kids have a built-in clock that drives them to develop on all these fronts, although not necessarily at the same rate. Letting them set the pace will help build up their confidence.

CHARTING THEIR PROGRESS The charts on the next three pages show some of the things your child may be able to do at different ages and gives tips on how you can help encourage their development. Remember, children develop at their own pace, so these are just general stages.

AROUND 12 TO 24 MONTHS

'WHAT I CAN DO NOW'

1 I'M LEARNING TO MOVE IN NEW WAYS

I can get around on my own – crawling, shuffling and then walking.

I can walk backwards.

I can pull a toy around with me.

I can carry a big toy when I walk.

I can bend down to pick something up on my own, though I'm a bit wobbly sometimes.

I've started to run.

I can stand on tiptoe.

I can kick a ball.

I can walk up and down stairs.

'WHAT YOU CAN DO TO HELP ME'

✷ Understand that my new skills make the world an exciting place.

✷ Make my surroundings safe because I don't have a sense of danger yet.

✷ Realise that going to the shops is a real adventure – I may want to climb up steps or on to a wall.

✷ Give me toys and other things from round the house that help me practise new things I can do.

✷ Help me develop physical skills – for example, by helping me get down from somewhere I've climbed.

AROUND 12 TO 24 MONTHS continued

'WHAT I CAN DO NOW'

'WHAT YOU CAN DO TO HELP ME'

2 I'M LEARNING TO CONTROL MY HANDS AND FINGERS

I can pick up tiny things like crumbs between my fingers and thumb.

I grasp toys but find it hard to let go.

I try to put blocks on top of each other.

I can scribble with a crayon or marker.

I'm very interested in how things work.

* Give me lots of finger foods, so I can feed myself.

* Let me drink from a cup.

* Take time when you dress me so I can put my arms in the sleeves.

* Give me a spoon to hold but be patient with me if I'm slow or make a mess.

* Let me have blocks so I can try to build a tower, and other toys and objects that allow me to practise my dexterity.

* Don't tell me off if I draw on the wall. To me it's no different to a piece of paper. Show me where I can draw.

* I'm learning fast but I still want you to play with me and help me do difficult things.

* I want to know about how things work, so give me the chance to figure things out for myself.

3 I'M LEARNING MORE ABOUT MYSELF AND OTHER PEOPLE

I can do simple tasks.

I can pull off some of my own clothes and help when you dress me.

I'm beginning to understand that one thing can be used as something else – so I might use a banana as a phone.

I want to be like you and my brothers and sisters.

I'm beginning to realise that I'm not you and you're not me.

I can recognise myself when I'm in a photo.

I'm beginning to like being with other kids.

If I can't get my own way I may push, hit or bite.

* Let me help you around the house by giving me simple but real jobs to do.

* Let me help when you dress and undress me.

* Play games of pretend but don't take over.

* Let me be around you as you do things and set me a good example to copy.

* Understand if I cry when you go away. I'm scared you won't come back. Tell me when you're coming back.

* Show me pictures of myself and the family and talk to me about them.

* Let me have other kids round to play or go to their houses, but don't expect me to play 'with' them yet.

* Don't expect me to know about sharing. Help by providing two toys.

* Understand that if I lash out it's because my feelings are strong. Show me other ways to get what I want.

Look at me, mum!

By 25 months your child is much more independent but they still need you – in a different way.

AROUND 25 TO 36 MONTHS

'WHAT I CAN DO NOW'

1 I'M LEARNING TO MOVE IN LOTS OF DIFFERENT NEW WAYS

I can climb on to a chair to look out of the window or reach something high up.
I can run and jump and go round things that are in my way.

I can walk up and down stairs putting one foot on each step.

I can kick a ball forward and throw it overhand.

I can balance on one foot for a few seconds.

I can sit on a small trike.

I can squat down and stand up again without using my hands.

'WHAT YOU CAN DO TO HELP ME'

✳ Make our home a safe place so I can explore and practise new things.

✳ Take me outdoors (perhaps to the park) so I can run, jump and climb.

✳ Be prepared for me to keep repeating new skills.

✳ Take me for walks and swimming and let me join in family games like football.

✳ Hold my hand when I go upstairs and remind me to hold on to the banister.

✳ Let me go up and down steps when we're out.

✳ Put on some music and let's dance to it.

✳ When we're out, talk to me about what we're doing so I can learn words I need.

✳ Help me understand ideas such as big and small, high and low, wet and dry.

✳ Get me a trike or other wheeled toy. A hand-me-down one is fine.

5 things to remember

✳ Your relationship with your child is important in helping them develop in a healthy way.

✳ Your tot's physical, mental and emotional growth are all linked and depend on each other.

✳ Their experiences of the world, including how you treat them, shapes their development.

AROUND 25 TO 36 MONTHS continued

'WHAT I CAN DO NOW'

2 I'M LEARNING FINER CONTROL OF MY HANDS AND FINGERS

I can turn the pages of a book one at a time.

I can build a tower of more than six blocks.

I can hold a pencil and scribble in circles as well as making a straight line going up and down or across the paper.

I can screw and unscrew lids.

I can turn a rotating handle.

I can sort objects by shape and colour.

I show a strong preference for using my right or my left hand.

'WHAT YOU CAN DO TO HELP ME'

✳ Read to me as much as you can and let me turn the pages.

✳ Give me blocks to play with and paper to draw on.

✳ Carry on giving me finger foods but let me use a spoon and fork if I want to.

✳ Let me help you prepare my food – I can wash fruit or snap green beans. I can mix things and even break eggs if you show me how.

✳ Let me help you lay the table for our meals.

✳ Let me pour the milk over my breakfast cereal.

✳ Use jars with safety caps if there's anything dangerous in them that I really shouldn't touch.

✳ Don't make me use my right hand if I prefer to use my left.

✳ I feel a whole range of emotions and I know when you're feeling them too.

✳ I usually don't mind leaving you for a while to go to a friend's or nursery.

✳ I find big changes in my routine difficult.

✳ Let me try out things for myself but know when to step in.

✳ When I do things you don't like, I'm not doing them to upset you.

✳ When I show you affection or sympathy, let me know how it makes you feel. Say, 'That was a lovely hug. I feel much better already.'

3 I'M LEARNING EVEN MORE ABOUT MYSELF AND OTHER PEOPLE

I like to play pretend games.

I like to copy adults and other kids.

If you stop me doing what I want, I may throw a tantrum.

I like to play with other kids.

I know when something is 'mine' or not – and I still have trouble sharing sometimes.

I'm beginning to have strong likes and dislikes for toys, colours and playmates.

✳ Understand that pretend play is how I learn about the world and join in.

✳ Set me a good example so I know how to behave.

✳ Don't worry if I copy things you do, like putting on make-up, if I'm a boy or dad shaving if I'm a girl. It helps me to understand the differences between people.

✳ If I copy behaviour that you don't like, don't tell me off but explain why instead.

✳ Let me spend time playing with other people so I can learn about making friends.

✳ Understand that when I have tantrums my feelings may frighten me. Try to ignore them.

✳ Let me play with other kids at home, at their house or nursery, so I can learn more about taking turns and sharing.

✳ Let me join in family meals so I can learn to enjoy eating with other people. Invite other kids to tea sometimes or let me go to their house.

✳ Have fun with me.

Kids vary a lot in the age at which they learn to do things but if your tot seems noticeably different to other kids or you just have a hunch that things aren't quite right, ask your health visitor for help.

We are family

Families come in many forms but get the basics right and your child will do well whatever the set-up.

> 'Reassure them that it's still OK for them to love the parent who is leaving.'
> *Jenny, divorced mum*

> 'If you're a step-mum, try to be a friend, not their mum.'
> *Nicola, mum and step-mum*

No one type of family is best for kids. There may, however, be additional factors to take into account if your family situation is changing.

When parents part No matter what age kids are if you divorce or separate, the change will have an impact. But if you handle the break-up sensitively and don't use your tot as a weapon in adult battles, they will cope.

It's vital to talk to kids about the separation in words they will easily understand and give them the time and space to deal with their upset. They need to know that both of you still love them and will continue to be involved in their lives.

Smart tips for separating parents
* Before you part, make plans for sharing parenting in the future. It's important the parent who is leaving has a clear, defined role.
* If you and your partner can't talk to each other, it's a good idea to get outside help with solving practical problems.
* Keep in touch with grandparents.
* Make sure you inform your tot's nursery and other groups.
* Try to keep your kids' daily life as familiar and stable as possible. Stick to their routines and have a consistent approach to discipline and treats.
* Be prepared for your tot to revert to more babyish behaviour for a time.

One on one It can be very tiring when there's no one else to share the responsibility, especially when there are big decisions involved. It's important to make time for yourself and to get as much emotional support as you can and all the practical, financial support you may be entitled to.

Smart tips for lone parents
* Don't be afraid to ask for help if you need it.
* Try to get out of the house regularly.
* Get your child used to being looked after by other people so they don't become overly dependent on you alone.

A step in time Being a step-parent is a minefield, and any two homes will have different expectations and rules. Building relationships takes time; if you're a step-parent, find things you can do with the child so you can get to know each other. Parents should spend time alone with their tot and talk about what's going on and how they feel about it.

EXPERT FILES *Child psychologist*

'It's hard being a parent and twice as hard when you're a lone parent. So it's important to try to make time for yourself each day. If you're near the end of your tether, put your child somewhere safe and take a short breather. Meet other grown-ups, maybe people with children so they can play while you natter. Use mother and toddler clubs, the library and anything else that gets you out of the house for a short time.'

Christine Puckering, Department of Child and Adolescent Psychiatry, Glasgow University

Your toddler is developing so fast and in so many ways that it's not surprising if you sometimes feel overwhelmed. But don't despair! In this section we look at common challenges you're likely to encounter, and how to smooth the way.

*troubleshooting
...those problems solved

WHAT YOU CAN FIND IN THIS SECTION

| UNDERSTANDING YOUR TODDLER | TANTRUMS | FOOD MATTERS | POTTY TRAINING | GOOD NIGHT | BROTHERS & SISTERS |

Getting to know

Toddlers all have similar milestones in their lives, but each child is unique. Your reactions will play a big part in whether your child grows up to see themselves and the world around them in a positive or negative light. Most children find some things a breeze and other things harder. As you get to know your child better, you'll be able to tell when they need a helping hand, and encourage them to find the best way to do things for themselves.

IDENTIFY THEIR MOODS

Experts who have studied children's personalities have identified several key temperamental traits. Pick the ones that you see in your tot, but bear in mind that they can quickly switch between moods. Your child may be active and boisterous in some situations, but quiet and cautious in others.
If difficult behaviour persists for any length of time, or if you get the feeling that something is not quite right, seek advice from your GP or health visitor.

IMPULSIVE AND CHANGEABLE

Do you find it easy to predict when your child is likely to feel hungry or tired or want to go to the toilet? Or do their habits seem to be all over the place?

TIPS AND TRICKS

✳ Establish a clear routine with regular eating and sleeping times. Structures and boundaries will help encourage them to organise their patterns.

✳ Be patient if it takes them time to settle back to normal after a change in their routine, such as a holiday, starting nursery or the birth of a new baby.

BUSY AND BOISTEROUS

How active is your child? Can it be hard to get them to sit still for a second, even to change their nappy? Do they charge through the day without a second to relax? Do they tend to act first and think later, and find it difficult to follow routines?

TIPS AND TRICKS

✳ Provide lots of active games, toys and outside play to help channel that boundless energy.

✳ Persevere with quiet activities, such as looking at a book. They may need help with learning to sit quietly.

QUIET AND CAUTIOUS

Is your child happy to sit quietly and watch what's going on? Do they sometimes prefer to stay in the background rather than being centre of attention?

TIPS AND TRICKS

✳ Build in some down times during the day when they can recharge their batteries in peace. Tell them in advance if you'll be going to noisy, busy places.

you

PATIENCE CAN PAY

How long does your child continue trying to do something hard? Do they generally carry on until they've found the last piece to the jigsaw? Or do they abandon it?

TIPS AND TRICKS

✱ Help your tot learn patience through games that involve taking turns, or activities such as baking, where they have to wait to see the results of their efforts.

✱ Show your child that it's worth carrying on by starting off with things you know they can do – and praise them when they finish.

✱ Offer encouragement and let them know that you believe they can complete things!

HEART ON THEIR SLEEVE

Does your little one react strongly and loudly to fairly minor events at times? Do they get really excited when they're happy and cry loudly if they're upset?

TIPS AND TRICKS

✱ Kids whose emotions are on the surface get a lot out of life but they can be exhausting. Build in some 'me time' after they've gone to bed.

✱ Take their feelings seriously and give them a chance to express them through telling stories, dressing-up games and singing songs. Listen if they need to talk.

SENSITIVE MOMENTS

How sensitive is your child to sights, sounds, tastes and touch? Do they react, either positively or negatively, to particular sounds, say the washing machine? Do they jump if something surprises them? Are they a faddy eater or will they tuck into anything?

TIPS AND TRICKS

✱ Be careful with clothes; that woolly jumper may be too itchy for them.

✱ Give them a variety of foods but don't insist that they have things they don't like.

✱ Encourage your child to use their senses positively by giving them paint and brushes, modelling clay and other sensory materials.

FULL OF LIFE

How easily is your tot distracted? Can you calm them down if they're upset by offering them something else to do? Do they soon get bored and do they find it hard to settle down to things that need concentration, such as a jigsaw?

TIPS AND TRICKS

✱ Learn to appreciate the positive side of their lively mind – fleeting attention can be a bonus when you want to divert them from doing something you don't want them to do!

✱ Help them complete a task if they need it, such as getting ready, to stop them getting sidetracked.

✱ Keep instructions and tasks clear and simple, and tackle one thing at a time.

Say what you mean

There's not always a right or wrong way of doing things, but what all toddlers need is structure and boundaries to make them feel safe and secure.

As your toddler grows more independent, they will begin to test the limits of what they can and can't do. Tough though it may be – for you both – this stage is an essential part of learning and adjusting to social situations. By allowing your child to develop in this way, you'll help them to discover new abilities, but also that what they want to do may sometimes be unsafe, and could also hurt or upset other people.

The boundaries you create are vital to help your kids feel safe and make the world seem more certain and easier to understand. No child can feel confident if they have unlimited freedom or responsibility. Having said that, they will test the boundaries you set. This is the way they begin to understand themselves and the world – which you may find challenging.

While there isn't one right way to go about things – every parent and child and every family is different – there are a few tried and tested tricks that can help make it easier to deal with your toddler's behaviour.

Be clear about your rules
Each family has its own rules – often unspoken – about what is acceptable, so the first step in helping your child to behave well is to decide on yours.

Then make sure your child knows what they are and remind them often.

Be consistent
Conflict can arise when parents, and others who care for your child, follow different sets of rules, so make sure everyone concerned knows what is expected of them. The same applies if you allow your tot to do something one day and then tell them off for doing the same thing the next. When you say 'No' make sure you mean it.

Expect them to behave well
Although it may not always seem like it, children love to please their parents. If you expect your child to behave badly, chances are they will. However, if they know that you expect them to behave well, they're much more likely to try to please.

Be realistic
You can't expect a toddler to know that the ornament you left within arm's reach isn't a toy to bang on the floor. Think ahead to avoid such problems. Put things you don't want them to touch out of temptation's way.

Try saying yes How many times have you said no today? Always being refused can lead to a build-up of frustration. Next time your toddler asks you a question, consider answering yes instead. For example, 'Yes, you can do it tomorrow,' or, 'Yes, after we've been shopping.'

Be clear and specific Make sure that your little one understands exactly what they are being asked to do. Instead of saying, 'Please can you tidy up now,' try, 'Pick up your books and put them on the shelf now,

please.' If there's no choice about something, don't confuse things by letting them think they can decide. Instead of saying, 'Do you want to have your bath now?', say, 'Now it's bath time.'

Actions speak louder than words If your tot does something against the rules, show them what they could have done instead. So if they draw on the wall, show them that the correct place to draw is on paper or on a blackboard. And if they get in a mess let them make amends by helping you to clear it up.

ask *christine*

Q My daughter Kylie's favourite word is no. It's driving me mad. Any tips? Simone, Dundee

A It's common for kids this age to go through a phase of refusing to do what you want. Where possible, let Kylie practise deciding things for herself – for example, whether to wear her red dress or her blue dress; whether to have a yogurt or fruit for pudding. Only make rules and demands that really matter to you, but then stick to them. Encourage her to compromise. For example tell her. 'We'll go to the playground after we've done the shopping,' or ' If you help me tidy your toys now, we'll read a story after tea'. You can also model by saying yes when you can or negotiating a solution. For example, 'Well you can't have a chocolate biscuit right before dinner, but what about an apple if you are really hungry?'.
Stay calm but stand your ground if it is important.

Reward good behaviour

✳ **Praise and attention work far better than criticism or punishment, so show that you're pleased when your child behaves well.**

✳ **If they tidy their toys without being asked, say, 'I'm really pleased you tidied away your toys. Now the room is nice and tidy and we've got more time for your story.'**

✳ **Let them hear you saying good things about them to other people.**

EXPERIENCED PARENTS

OLD HAND Experienced mums have found it helpful to put their children's feelings into words before they have the ability to explain things for themselves.

NEW HAND If you've got into the habit of nagging it may take time to change their behaviour, but persevere with giving praise and you will succeed.

FIRST-TIME PARENTS

Rise above the tantrums. They won't last for ever. Here's how to stay sane and cool.

If there's one thing toddlers do well, it's throwing a tantrum. The peak time for tantrums is around two years old. With good management they will usually begin to fade by three, and by age four most toddlers have worked out that there are better ways to get what they want. A full-on temper tantrum is tough for you and frightening for your child. The good news is that a few simple strategies will prevent or contain most of your child's tantrums.

Why tantrums happen

It may seem as if your little one is having a tantrum out of spite, to attract attention and to cause you maximum embarrassment and annoyance. Nothing could be further from the truth. Tantrums express the frustrations of being a toddler. At this age, children are learning to do many things, from talking to controlling their bodily functions. They want to do so much, but are often held back by their capabilities. At the same time, they're grappling with the rules of the world – and the fact that some things are not allowed. Because your little one can't tell you what they're feeling inside, they end up screaming and throwing themselves around. But although a toddler in the throes of a tantrum can seem all-powerful, they may be scared by the intensity of their rage. However helpless you may feel, you are the one in charge and need to do everything possible to get that message across. That doesn't mean having a tantrum yourself, shouting or smacking your child. These are actually signs that you are out of control. What it does mean is being prepared for tantrums and drawing up a tantrum strategy in advance.

Tantrum control

Try to prevent tantrums by giving praise. Your time and attention are the most important things to your child, so if they learn to get lots of it by throwing a tantrum, they'll continue down that path. Instead, reinforce good behaviour whenever you see it by giving them praise and cuddles and kisses.

Spotting the early warning signs of a tantrum is the key to stopping them spiralling out of control. Try to become aware of triggers such as tiredness, hunger, excess heat or cold and, where

4 questions to ask

If your child is throwing lots of tantrums, it may help to analyse why they are happening. Ask yourself the following:

* What triggered the tantrum?

* What did your child do during the tantrum?

* How did you react?

* What was the outcome?

temper

possible, try to avoid situations that you know are likely to spark an outburst, such as supermarket checkouts and busy shopping centres. Use distraction if you see your child gearing up for a tantrum. Sing a funny song, suggest they help to look for a toy or take them to another room – anything that shifts their attention. Giving them a choice over some aspects of their life can help stop tension building up. You could allow them to make certain decisions, such as what shoes to wear or whether to brush their teeth before or after their bath. If they make choices that aren't important they feel they have some input, without you losing your authority.

HOW IT WORKS FOR ME

With a tantrum, you have to watch the signs and try to catch it quickly. Distraction worked very well with Kieran.

Suzanne, mum to Callum, nine, Kieran, five, and Rachael, two

When we were at the shops, I'd get Kieran out of the buggy and ask him to help me pack the bags to keep him busy. Or I'd let him walk with me and make our trip as interesting as possible – like talking to him about which shop we were going to next. Children can get bored sitting in a buggy. Now that Rachael, my two-year-old, can walk, she doesn't like being in the buggy, either. So I'll run with it and turn it into a game. She tells me when to stop and go – I don't care how stupid I look! If your child is screaming, other parents stare at you and it can be very stressful and really embarrassing. But when I know my child's not coming to any harm, I think, 'Who cares? Your child went through it too.'

OLD HAND Experienced mums know that a child's tantrum triggers will be different to their sibling's. Each child has different flashpoints.

NEW HAND **First-time** mums should be prepared for a toddler's tantrum triggers to change and develop. Try to deal with new ones calmly as they appear.

Lucy and Beth go to the newsagents...

1 Lucy and daughter Beth, two, are at the newsagent looking for a birthday card, when Beth spots some sweets.

MUM THINKS: 'Oh no – why do they put sweets there where she can see them?'

BETH THINKS: 'I can see sweets. I want some of those.'

2 Beth ask her mum for sweets and when Lucy says no the temperature rises fast. As she feels more under pressure, Lucy takes a tougher line.

'Want sweets. Want s-w-e-e-t-s!'

'Beth want sweets.'

'No, you can't have any. We've got to get a birthday card for Nana.'

'Stop it this minute! Everyone's looking at you. We've got to get Nana's card.'

tantrum

Follow our step-by-step story of a tantrum. Recognise it?

Remember
* Praise your child when you see them doing something well.
* Be clear and calm about what you expect.
* Don't be embarrassed – tantrums happen to the best parents.
* Stay firm and ignore the behaviour. Don't argue or reason.
* Make sure your child is safe. Once the tantrum is in retreat, reassure your child and carry on with what you were doing before.

3 Beth works herself up into a full-blown tantrum – to the horror of other customers. Although she's embarrassed, Lucy knows it's best to ignore a tantrum and wait for it to pass.

'BETH WANT SWEETS!'

4 After what seems like an age, Beth starts to calm down. To distract her, a relieved Lucy suggests that Beth choose the card.

'When you've calmed down, I'd really like you to help me find a card for Nana.'

'I can see you were really upset about those sweets. Come on now, let's get a card for Nana.'

'I'll tell you what, let's see who can find the nicest card for Nana.'

5 Beth picks out a card and toddles over to Lucy, tantrum forgotten…

Things to think about
* How well do you think Lucy handled the tantrum?
* Could she have done anything differently?
* How might the tantrum have been avoided?

✱ RESULT!

Feed 'em well

A healthy diet will keep your child fit for life – and now is the best time to start good habits.

TOPTIP
To avoid tooth decay give them water or milk to drink. Avoid sugary drinks or fruit squashes between meals and before bedtime.

Food – where would your little one be without it? As well as helping them grow strong and healthy, food helps them to use their hands, mouth and senses, learn about making choices, and social skills such as sharing, taking turns and talking. The starting point for a healthy diet is attractive meals in manageable portions.

3 important things you need to digest

✳ Helping your child learn to enjoy healthy foods could help reduce their risk of obesity, heart disease, high blood pressure and diabetes in later life.

✳ Always wash your hands before handling food. This will help prevent you and your toddler from getting tummy aches and other illnesses.

✳ Add variety by providing a good mix of textures and tastes and vary the way you cook. Skip the fry-ups and try grilling, stir-frying, stewing and steaming and serving some raw salads or finger foods.

ON THE GRID Your child needs foods from four main groups every day to maintain a healthy diet, and here's how to ensure they get them. There's plenty of choice – even for the fussiest tots!

Food group:	Needed for:	Try:	Servings per day:
Dairy and calcium-rich foods	Calories, protein, vitamins and minerals such as calcium	Milk, cheese, yoghurt, fromage frais, milk puddings, tofu, tahini and calcium-enriched milk alternatives	3
Meat, fish and alternatives	Protein, vitamins and minerals	Beef, pork, chicken, lamb, turkey, fish such as salmon, haddock or tuna, eggs, baked beans, chickpeas, lentils, peas and beans	2
Fruit and vegetables	Vitamin C, fibre and other protective vitamins and minerals	Apples, pears, satsumas, grapes, melon, plums, mangoes, bananas Peas, broccoli, tomatoes, carrots, courgettes, mushrooms	Aim for 5 a day, of which 2 should be veg – fresh, frozen, canned and dried all count
Bread and other cereals and potatoes	Calories, vitamins, minerals and fibre	Rice, bread, pasta, breakfast cereals, potatoes, sweet potatoes	4 (ideally, including some wholemeal and wholegrain varieties)

Limits
Go easy on the following:

✳ SUGAR Found in sweets, biscuits, cakes, doughnuts, fruit squashes.

✳ CAFFEINE Found in coffee, tea, cola and some fizzy drinks.

✳ SALT Found in crisps, salted snacks, bacon and other processed meats.

NEW HAND Remember, there isn't any food your tot has to eat. If they don't like something, don't force it. Instead, find an alternative they do like.

FIRST-TIME PARENTS

OLD HAND Just because an older child was a faddy eater, don't assume a younger one will be too. Treat each child as an individual.

EXPERIENCED PARENTS

Food, glorious food

Eat well as a family and your toddler will soon learn to take pleasure in food and mealtimes.

Food and eating can be really enjoyable for your toddler, especially if you set a good example as a family by all eating in the same way. This may mean you need to take a look at what you're eating too!

How much is enough? The amount your little one eats depends on their size and how much they run about. Toddlers grow more slowly than babies, but they still have growth spurts – often around the time they start to walk or after they've had to fend off an illness. Toddlers can devour everything in sight one day and pick like a bird the next. Provided they're growing at a healthy rate, there's no need to worry. The same applies if they seem to live on just a few foods. As long as a range of healthy choices are on offer, most kids seem to balance their food intake over time.

Little and often Most kids like to eat little and often. That's because they have tiny stomachs so it's easier for them to cope with three smaller meals and a few snacks rather than three big meals.

It's important that they don't feel overwhelmed and that you spot when they're full. As long as you're not filling them up with sweets or drinks between meals, you'll soon get to know their eating pattern.

HOW IT WORKS FOR ME

One of the best tips I was given is to be more flexible. I used to think Finn should have something cooked for lunch, but if he won't eat it what's the point?

Lynsey, 31, mum to Finn, two and a half

Food is the biggest challenge in our life at the moment. If Finn doesn't like something it becomes a total drama. We've tried ignoring him, encouraging him, rewarding him and putting him on the 'naughty step' but none of it really seems to work. He hates being put out of the kitchen but he'll still come back to the table and refuse to touch his food. He can be extremely stubborn when he wants to be and I'm aware that I have to take a step back and think about how I react. I try to limit how much processed food he has but it's not easy. He controls his whole diet. I suppose it's one of the few things he can control, but I find it very hard.

For example, there's no way he'll put baked beans in his mouth. He'll eat chicken and ham and he loves grapes and oatcakes but even if he's eaten something before, there's no guarantee that he'll eat it again. He might eat pizza one night say, but not the next. One of the best tips I was given is to be more flexible. I used to think he had to have something cooked for lunch, but if he won't eat it what's the point? So now I might give him a stick of cheddar, an oatcake and fruit instead. I also give him vitamin drops (A, C and D). Vitamin D can be made by the body from sunlight but in winter there isn't enough sun, so drops are important.

TOP TIP

If your tot isn't keen on veg, you can disguise it with cheese sauce or add to a tomato sauce for pasta.

WHAT'S ON THE MENU?
We looked at the food intake of three Scottish toddlers on a typical day. Top marks all round!

Menu 1
Lewis, 18 months

BREAKFAST
Small glass of unsweetened orange juice, diluted half and half with water. Bowl of Weetabix with milk. Slice of wholemeal bread with spread.

MORNING SNACK
Cup of milk. Toast fingers with spread. Tangerine.

LUNCH
Chicken breast and mashed potato. Banana and custard.

AFTERNOON SNACK
Cup of water. Sliced apple dipped in yoghurt.

TEA
Cheese on toast with tomatoes.

Tinned peaches in juice.

Menu 2
Ellie, 26 months (vegetarian)

BREAKFAST
Unsweetened orange juice, diluted half and half with water. Scrambled egg on toast.

MORNING SNACK
Cup of water. Bread sticks, cubed cheese and apple chunks.

LUNCH
Spaghetti with tomato and vegetable sauce, grated cheese and broccoli. Tinned rice pudding with dried apricots.

AFTERNOON SNACK
Milk. Cream crackers with cheese. Apple.

TEA
Baked beans on toast with chopped tomatoes.

Menu 3
Kyle, 36 months

BREAKFAST
Unsweetened orange juice, diluted half and half with water. Baked beans and toasted muffin.

MORNING SNACK
Milk. Crumpet with spread. Orange segments.

LUNCH
Ham and tomato roll with carrot sticks.

AFTERNOON SNACK
Water. Pineapple in juice with plain yoghurt.

TEA
Fish in cheese sauce (ready-made or frozen), boiled potatoes and beans. Stewed apple.

---

ask christine

Q My 20-month-old son Logan won't eat anything I make. I'm at my wits' end. What do I do?
Isla, 24, Inverness

A If Logan is healthy and growing well, chances are he's getting what he needs. Research shows that toddlers may eat an unbalanced diet one day but make up for it the next. Most toddlers go through not liking something! Avoid having chocolate, sweet and crisps in the cupboard if you don't want him to have them. Try to get him interested by involving him in preparing food. Your attitude to food matters – join him at the table rather than leaving him to eat alone. Children eat better and are more likely to stay at the table if they have company. Limit choices to two, for example, 'Would you like peas or carrots today?'. Don't confuse him with too much choice and simply take away things he leaves without fuss.

Snack attack

Bin the crisps and try some of these tasty snacks:

* Bite-sized chunks of apple or pear
* Segments of seedless satsuma
* Carrot, pepper or courgette sticks
* Slices of cherry tomato
* Squares of toast, breads, rolls, baps with butter or spread
* Mini sandwiches with yeast extract, tuna, cheese or mashed banana
* Bread sticks with a dip or soft cheese
* Mini pizza triangles
* Oatcakes, rice cakes, crackers or crispbreads
* Natural yoghurt and fromage frais
* Muffins, crumpets, pancakes, potato or cheese scones
* Unsalted popcorn

EXPERT FILES *Health visitor*

'We all have days when we don't fancy what's on our plate, and toddlers are no different. Sit down with them, offer small manageable amounts of appropriate food and, if they use their fingers and make a mess, don't fret. Remember, fingers were invented before knives and forks! Your toddler will have fickle moments, but most tots grow well despite seemingly limited diets. Seek advice from your health visitor or public health nurse if you're worried.'

Margaret Duncan, Sure Start health visitor, Dundee

Teatime is fun time!

A few simple rules can help you avoid mealtime misery – and tame the tyrant in the high chair!

Food and mealtimes are a common battleground. This is one of the few areas where your toddler can express their growing independence and have control. In addition, small children are often naturally suspicious of new tastes and textures.

Faddy eating is usually more of an issue for parents than it is for toddlers. As long as your child is growing and has lots of energy, they're almost certainly meeting their nutritional needs. In fact, research shows that left to their own devices – and provided they're offered healthy choices – kids will almost always balance their food intake over the course of time.

OLD HAND Some children like to take things slowly. Have patience if your toddler takes longer than others in the family to get to the end of a meal.

NEW HAND It often helps if you make food look nice by cutting or slicing it. It will make eating a much more enticing activity for most toddlers.

GET FOODWISE

Think small Toddlers can be daunted by large portions. Keep servings small and appetising so eating doesn't seem like a big task. Cut finger foods into bite-sized pieces that are easy for little hands to pick up.

Stay calm If your toddler rejects a particular food – or even a whole meal – remember, it's the food they're rejecting, not you. If your child doesn't want to eat, take the food away without a fuss.

Make food fun Cutting foods into shapes or colouring them with fruit or vegetable juice can make some kids more likely to eat.

Be patient Toddlers tend to be naturally unadventurous. Experts say they may need to come across a new food five to 15 times before they're willing to eat it. So if your tot turns up their nose at something new, calmly take it away. You can try serving it again another time.

HOW IT WORKS FOR ME

> To encourage them to eat healthily I make up a chart for breakfast, dinner and tea and if they eat everything they get a big tick.

Mandy Ley, 38, mother of Rhaigan, three, Ross, six, Kelly, 21 months

Rhaigan eats everything I put on her plate, whereas Ross has never liked eating vegetables. To encourage them to eat healthily I make up a chart for mealtimes and if they eat everything they get a big tick. If they leave anything they get a cross.

If they get ticks in all the boxes they get a treat – nothing big, just praise at the end of the day. If they're ever not eating it really works. I've also cut down on what I put on their plates – if they see too much they tend not to want to eat it. I have some little bits on the side so that if they want more they can ask for it.

My health visitor told me to let them have two snacks during the day – healthy things such as sandwiches, fruit and yoghurt, rather than one big fat meal at the end of the day, and that also helps.

Don't bribe Bribing, forcing or rewarding your child for eating is never a good idea. If you promise your child a biscuit for eating lunch, you are teaching them that lunch is a punishment and the biscuit is a reward.

Let them help Helping prepare a meal will make your child feel more part of things. Even young toddlers can be enlisted to tear the lettuce for a salad or wash fruit. Older ones can help with mixing and laying the table.

Make it special Children like to be independent and love having small bowls of their own finger foods, such as strips of cheese, toast fingers, raisins and chopped cold meat, as an alternative to a formal family meal.

Keep it simple Don't waste time and energy creating over-elaborate meals. You can't beat fresh food that tastes and looks good.

Set a good example Kids learn by observation. If you're a faddy eater yourself your child may become one too.

Don't expect manners It's unrealistic to expect toddlers to have table manners. It's natural for a young child to want to squash their food and explore it with their fingers. Put a stout bib on them, protect the floor with a plastic tablecloth and don't fret. They'll get tidier in their eating habits as they get older!

Know when to call it a day If your child stops eating, turns away or gives you other signs that they've had enough, it's time to call a halt. Trying to force children to carry on eating when they've had enough just gets everyone cross and grouchy.

Stay cool about mess Finger feeding is fun but, like all feeding at this stage, it can be messy. Instead of fretting about sticky fingers, give in to the fact that mess is all part of the fun and experience of eating, and resist the urge to constantly wipe hands and mouth!

Is mealtime a battleground?

✳ Is your child growing and thriving? If the answer is yes, there's no need to worry.

✳ Are they filling up on drinks? Too much juice or milk could be filling their tummies. Gradually cut down and give plain water instead.

✳ Have healthy snacks to hand. High-calorie ones like sweets, biscuits and crisps could be denting your tot's appetite for healthier fare.

✳ Protect teeth from decay by making sure sugary food and drinks are eaten with a meal rather than between meals.

TOPTIP
Eating in a group with family or playmates encourages the social aspects of mealtimes, and children learn by example.

Don't let toilet training drive you potty

When it comes to potty training, it's all about timing. Get that right and they'll be dry before you know it.

After a couple of years of buying disposables or washing terry nappies, you probably can't wait for your little one to be potty trained. But don't be in too much of a hurry. The secret to success is to wait until your child is physically and emotionally ready. Follow their cues and don't be fazed if other children learn to use the potty earlier than yours. Many children start at around two, but each child differs, so stay calm and don't rush them into it.

Getting started

Starting toilet training is a common source of anxiety. Patience is essential to getting it right. Once you feel your child has got a rough idea of what it's all about, get a potty or toddler toilet seat and step – whichever you plan to use – and let them get used to it. At first, they'll probably use it as a toy. You can encourage them to find out what it's really

3 clues that your child is ready for potty training

* **They tell you they want to do a wee or a poo.** At first, this may be after rather than before the event! But at least they're becoming aware of their bowel and bladder movements.

* **Longer spells between wet nappies.** They have sa wet or dirty nappy after a meal or drink and can then be dry for a good few hours.

* **They show that they're aware of bodily functions.** They imitate you going to the toilet or show some other sign that they are aware of what's going on inside their body.

TOP TIP
Make sure everyone who cares for your child knows they're potty training and tell them the words you and your child use for the toilet.

for by playing at putting a doll or a teddy on it. Kids this age love to copy you so let them come with you when you go to the toilet. Talk about what you're doing in simple

'I had no idea how to start toilet training Jess but my sister, who potty trained her daughter, suggested letting her sit on the pot with her clothes on at first to help her get the idea. It worked a treat.' *Sara, 28, Perth*

'I noticed that Duncan was dry after his afternoon nap, so I suggested he sat on the potty. Result! After that there was no stopping him.' *Alison, 24, Ullapool*

'I got quite good at noticing when Anna was about to go and encouraging her to sit on the potty. It didn't take her long to get the hang of it and then she started asking for the pot herself.' *Rosie, 20, Dumfries*

terms and perhaps let them use the flush if they're not scared by the noise. Avoid words like 'dirty' that may cause your child to feel unclean.

Be patient and try not to expect too much, too soon. You may find your tot masters their bladder before their bowels, or the other way around. It will all work out with time.

POTTY TRAINING WITHOUT THE TEARS
Here's what to do to avoid toilet tears and tantrums

Time it right Pick a period when you have plenty of time. If your tot's about to start nursery, you've just moved house, are going on holiday, have just had another baby or are going through other changes, it's best to leave it until things are less hectic. Also, be consistent – don't chop and change from nappies to pants or knickers during the day.

Be prepared If you live in a house, keep a potty upstairs and one downstairs. Be sure to have a potty with you when you're out and about. It's a good idea to keep one in the car too and to take a set of spare clothes out with you.

Don't hang about At first, when your tot needs to go they need to go now, so don't ignore it when the call comes. As they get older they will be able to wait longer. Make it easy on yourself. The summer months can be an easier time to try potty training, as your little one can run around without nappies. Bathtime is another good time to introduce the pot. Make a note of your child's pattern of bowel movements so you can pick the best times of day to suggest using it.

Get the clothes right You don't want to spend ages changing your toddler's clothes, so make sure what they're wearing is easy to remove.

Let them set the pace If you know when your child is likely to want to use the potty, encourage them to sit down. But make sure they feel it is their choice – you'll be well aware that toddlers like to feel they are in control!

Be prepared for accidents
Accidents are par for the course during potty training. When it happens, change their clothes straight away and calmly encourage them to have a go on the potty or toilet next time. Do the same thing, even if you thought you had it sorted. They'll get there in time!

Encourage them with praise
As always, praise is your child's best teacher. Say something like, 'You were a big boy/girl to use the potty,' but don't make a big deal of it. For example, don't reward them with food or toys. Ignore the odd lapse and never tell them off for failing to use the potty or having an accident.

EXPERT FILES *Health visitor*

'Potty training is a subject that everyone has an opinion on. The important thing is for you to recognise when your child is ready. Forcing children to use the potty or toilet can do more harm than good, so take it slowly. Watch for your child showing signs that they recognise the need to go – brain and bladder need to work together, so do it at the child's pace and have a stress-free time!'

Margaret Duncan, Sure Start health visitor, Dundee

Good night, sleep tight

You want them to sleep but it's the last thing on their mind. So how do you get a silent night?

Sleep – or rather, lack of it – is a common problem for parents. For your toddler, the world is an exciting place with tons of new things to learn every day, so sleep can seem like a dull and unwanted interruption. At this age, your child will also realise that they're an individual, and separate from mum and dad. So if you leave, they may fear being left alone for good – a scary thought indeed.

On top of all this, it is becoming apparent to your playful bundle of joy that playing up at bedtime is a great way to wind up the grown-ups. But don't despair – peaceful nights are just a few simple steps away.

Routine matters The single most important thing you can do to ensure that your toddler, and the rest of the family, gets a good night's sleep is to establish a simple and consistent bedtime routine. It's up to you to develop your own regime, but it could go like this:

Teatime Talk to your child about how they are going to get ready for bed now.
✳ Play a quiet game, and talk about what you did today and any plans you have for tomorrow.
✳ Give them a warm bath, put the lights on low, keep distractions to a minimum and clean their teeth.
✳ Put pyjamas on them in their bedroom.
✳ Finish with a story (again, nothing too exciting) or a gentle song or rhyme.
✳ Kiss and cuddle them and say 'Goodnight' or 'I love you' then leave the room with confidence and without fuss.

TOPTIP
As long as your child is safe and not very distressed it won't hurt them to cry for a few minutes if they wake at night. It encourages them to learn to soothe themselves rather than relying on you.

Time for a nap? Toddlers need a daytime nap or two. Typically, a one-year-old needs about an hour in the morning and in the afternoon. A two-year-old usually needs an hour or so in the afternoon, but by three most tots are fine with a short nap in the afternoon or none at all.

Somewhere between 15 and 18 months your child may reach a stage where one nap doesn't seem enough but two is too much. The same may happen around the age of three, when they can drop their nap altogether. Don't worry – the problem will sort itself out.

Meanwhile, if they fall asleep in the pushchair don't disturb them. It sometimes helps during these transition periods to make bedtime a bit earlier. Even if your tot doesn't actually sleep during the day, some quiet time after lunch should help to relax and revive them.

ask christine

Q My two-year-old daughter, Maya, keeps climbing out of her cot. Do you think it's t ime to move her to a bed? And how should I go about it?
Julie, Strathclyde

A Most toddlers are ready to move to a bed of their own between the ages of about two and three, and Maya is showing you in no uncertain terms that she has reached that stage. You can help to prepare her by involving her in choosing some 'big-girl' bedding.

On the day of the move, let her help you make up her new bed and surround it with her favourite toys. Follow her usual bedtime routine. Wish her 'goodnight' firmly, and leave the room in a confident way. If she gets out of bed, take her back to bed straight away. Tell her you'll come back to check on her, and make sure you do. You might also want to use guardrails at first.

EXPERT FILES *Health visitor*

'Children need to learn to go to sleep and will benefit from a bedtime routine. Give them a bath, a story, colouring-in or perhaps a jigsaw, and have them cuddled in bed within 20 to 30 minutes. Any longer and they'll have forgotten why they put their PJs on!'

Margaret Duncan, Sure Start health visitor, Dundee

HOW MUCH IS ENOUGH? Toddlers vary a lot in the amount of sleep they need. The following is a rough guide.

Your child's age	Total hours needed	Hours at night	Suggested naps
12 months	13½	11½	2
18 months	12½	11½	1
24 months	12	11	1
36 months	11	10	1

SLEEP RULES Don't let your tot rule you!

Keep it down Try to keep things calm and quiet in the hour or so before bedtime, so they get in the mood to rest.

Curb your enthusiasm Avoid rough and tumble games and scary stories and TV programmes.

Gently does it Warn them it's nearly bedtime so that it doesn't come as a surprise.

Beds are for sleeping Never confuse the issue of sleeping by sending your little one to their cot or bed as a punishment.

Get in the groove Stick to a regular bedtime. Kids sleep best if they go to bed and get up at around the same time every day.

No soft options Don't let your child become reliant on drinks, TV or habits like being patted or rocked to sleep.

Hold your nerve Changes in routine – as a result of teething, illness, the arrival of a new baby, Christmas or a holiday – can disrupt sleep patterns. Be prepared for this and try not to get into bad habits. If you behave consistently, they'll soon go back to their usual routine.

Warning signs If your child seems irritable during the day it's likely that they're over-tired. Try putting them to bed slightly earlier.

Can't sleep won't sleep

Over-excitement or bad habits can quickly lead to sleep problems. Here's how to get round them.

Routine is never more critical than at bedtime. Bad habits are hard to break – so don't be tempted to take the easy way out.

PROBLEM: HE WON'T GO TO BED

* Why? Bedtime strike is common at this age. Developmental changes can affect sleep patterns. And the sheer excitement of all the new things your tot is learning to do can make it hard to let go at the end of the day.

SOLUTIONS:

* Establish a bedtime routine (see previous page) to help your little one get in the mood for sleep.
* Make sure your child is getting enough exercise to tire them out in the day – but avoid over-stimulation too close to bedtime.
* Make sure the space where they sleep is nice.
* Once you've put them to bed, say goodnight and leave the room quickly.
* Be consistent. If your child keeps getting out of bed, gently help them back without fuss, chat or attention – however many attempts it takes.
* Don't give in by bringing them into the living room or letting them watch TV.
* Avoid them becoming over-tired by ensuring they get a daytime nap (or two) if still needed.

PROBLEM: SHE WAKES IN THE NIGHT

* Why? We all briefly surface as we go through cycles of lighter and deeper sleep, but toddlers sometimes wake up fully during one of the lighter cycles and find it hard to drop back off again.

SOLUTIONS:

* Leave them alone for a short while to see if they can settle themselves.
* If they don't, go in and settle them down gently, then say 'Goodnight' firmly and leave the room. You may need to repeat this several times. Each time they cry, leave it a bit longer before you go in and calm them down.
* Don't give in and whatever you do don't reward them for waking up by taking them out of their room.

PROBLEM: SHE KEEPS COMING INTO OUR BED

* Why? Because she can get away with it. One way toddlers can exert their growing independence is by getting out of their bed and coming into yours. They will carry on unless you put a stop to it.

SOLUTIONS:

* During the day say to your child, 'Everyone sleeps in their own bed at night.' Difficult though it may be, and however tired you are, if they get up or come into your bed, take them back and settle them down gently but firmly. Then go back to bed.
* Be prepared to repeat this and don't give in. After a few nights they should get the idea. You might want to reward them for staying in bed by using a star chart.

PROBLEM: HE'S SCARED OF THE DARK

* Why? At this age your little one is developing an active imagination.

SOLUTIONS:

* Avoid scary TV programmes or stories.
* Use a night-light.
* If they awake from a nightmare, stay with them for a bit and explain that it was just a dream.
* If your child is waking regularly with nightmares, ask them if they are upset or worried about anything. A stressful event, such as starting nursery or the arrival of a new baby, may be the cause. Talk to your doctor or health visitor if their nightmares persist.

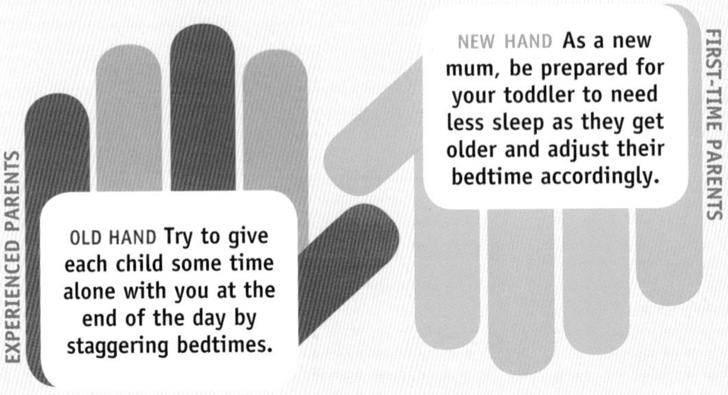
EXPERIENCED PARENTS
OLD HAND Try to give each child some time alone with you at the end of the day by staggering bedtimes.
FIRST-TIME PARENTS
NEW HAND As a new mum, be prepared for your toddler to need less sleep as they get older and adjust their bedtime accordingly.

New arrival

Prepare your toddler for a new addition to the family and you'll be spared tears later.

The arrival of another baby is bound to be a bit of an upheaval, but with preparation you can make it a happy event for the whole family.

The key is to involve your child right from the word go. Let them feel your tummy and talk about how the baby inside is growing – but don't push it if they're not interested. Show them where their baby brother or sister will sleep after they're born and ask them for help with choosing newborn supplies, like clothes and toys.

TOP TIP

When you talk to your toddler about the new baby, put them centre-stage by saying 'your little brother/sister' rather than 'my new baby'.

Tell it like it is Realistically, they won't be able to play with them at first. Talk about what babies are like and what they can and can't do. Take your child to visit other families with babies to help them learn what to expect.

Keep things stable Make sure they spend plenty of time with the person who will look after them when you go into labour, and any other carers. Be sure you tell your child that some things won't change – for example, going to nursery or going to their gran's on Wednesday.

Plan well ahead Make any changes, such as moving from a cot to a bed, well in advance so they don't feel ousted. Never say, 'You have to move out of your cot for the baby.' Avoid major changes, such as potty training or starting nursery, too close to the delivery date.

First meeting When your toddler meets their new brother or sister for the first time, try to arrange for the new baby to be in the cot rather than your arms. It's best to let your child set the pace. If they want to hold the baby help them to do so – but don't insist on it.

Be tolerant If your older child says they hate the baby or want to send it back, don't criticise or tell them off. Acknowledge their feelings and help them work through them. Try saying something like, 'Sounds like you wish things were the same as before your baby brother/sister came. Come here and let's have a hug'.

ask *christine*

Q We're planning another baby. When should I tell my two-year-old? Sue, 21

A As soon as you suspect you're pregnant, introduce the idea of families and point out brothers and sisters so your child starts to see them as part of everyday life. It's best to break the news at the same time as you tell other people so they don't learn by chance. However, nine months is a long time for a three-year-old. Try to give a sense of when the baby is due, in the summer for example.

Q Since my daughter Amie was born my son Liam has been so clingy. He wants to suck from her bottle and has started waking at night. Julie, 27

A It's common for toddlers to be babyish after a sibling is born. They may want to suck from a bottle or the breast, start wetting themselves, wake at night or have tantrums. Try to ignore bad behaviour and give attention for good. Get Liam involved, for example 'Liam, can you find me the baby wipes?'. Take every chance to praise him for being a big brother and set aside some time to spend with him doing 'big boy' things.

Friend or foe?

Fights between brothers and sisters over toys and territory are inevitable, but a few clever tactics can smooth the ruffles.

If your home is like a war zone, don't despair. It's normal for brothers and sisters to fight and it's one of the ways they learn to share, take turns and get on with other people. Follow our tips for defusing quarrels.

Give them one-to-one time
Try to spend time alone with each of your children – perhaps at bedtime or when your older child is at nursery or school.

Give them private space
Try to give each child a private place in which to keep their things. If you don't have separate bedrooms let them have a drawer, corner of the room or box for their bits and pieces.

Be fair Never compare your children or hold one of them up as an example. 'Why can't you be more like your brother/sister?' is a hurtful thing to say to any child, whatever their age.

Stay out of it When squabbles break out, try to keep your distance and give them a chance to resolve things on their own. Whatever you do, don't take sides.

Put a stop to violence Make it absolutely clear that you won't tolerate abusive behaviour. If things get ugly, separate your kids calmly and insist on them spending time in separate rooms to simmer down.

Keep your cool Try to remain calm. If you get angry yourself you're giving them attention for bad behaviour, which risks making it worse.

Make expectations clear
Let your kids know that while you don't expect them to be best pals the whole time, you do expect them to respect each other's differences, share, and talk things through rather than fighting.

TOP TIP
Stay calm. If you get angry you're giving attention for bad behaviour, which risks making it worse.

you say

'Because my children are different ages and sexes, most of the time they play side by side without too many problems, but sometimes he insists on taking her toys and then all hell breaks loose. It used to worry me, but I've learned it's best to try to ignore it and usually it stops.'
Romey, 19, mum to Rebecca, three, and Mathew, one

EXPERT FILES *Health visitor*

'All children will try to compete and assert their authority – whether they're the youngest or the oldest – just to remind everyone that they're there. Try doing things that everyone in the family can join in with, whatever their age, letting each of them see what the other is good at. It'll also cheer you up as a parent to see your children enjoying time together.'

Margaret Duncan, Sure Start health visitor, Dundee

You're in a unique position to be a good influence on your toddler's health, not only now but all through their life. Even so, all kids get ill from time to time and most have the occasional accident. This section is about how you can help to keep your child safe and healthy every step of the way.

*keep them healthy
...getting it right

WHAT YOU CAN FIND IN THIS SECTION

DAILY HEALTH CARE	MINOR ILLNESSES	SUPPORT FOR SPECIAL NEEDS

Head to

TOP TIP
Praise your tot for cleaning their teeth but ensure that you always do the main brushing until at least age seven.

Minor health problems are normal for most toddlers but you can keep them to a minimum by making healthcare part of your daily routine.

FEET
* Let your tot go around barefoot indoors (make sure your floor is clean and safe). This encourages their feet to develop properly.

* For outdoors, choose comfy, lightweight shoes with flexible, non-skid soles.

* Have their feet measured every six to eight weeks because they're growing rapidly at this time.

* Always make sure that your child's socks fit – tight socks can damage feet too.

* Keep an eye on toenails and always cut them straight across the top.

* If something is wrong with your child's feet or they're walking strangely, talk to your health visitor or GP.

URINARY/GENITAL
* Keep the genital area clean and use a barrier cream to prevent nappy rash if needed.

* If a rash develops, let them go around with their nappy off and ask your health visitor for advice.

* Watch out for threadworms. They look like little white threads (hence the name) in the bowel motions. Your pharmacist or health visitor will be able to suggest treatments.

* Seek medical advice from your health visitor or GP if your child is frequently constipated, has loose stools or blood in their stools.

SKIN
* Wipe your child's face and hands gently before and after eating. Be careful of their delicate skin! Don't use baby wipes all the time.

* Keep nails short.

* Give them a daily bath, dry them well and apply body moisturiser if needed.

* In summer, smooth on a sunscreen with a Sun Protection Factor of at least 15 and dress them in light, loose clothes and a hat.

* Always put on more sunscreen after your child has been in water.

HAIR
* Keep hair clean and brushed or combed.

* Make hair washing a game and prevent tears at bathtime by using a shampoo shield or flannel.

* Watch out for headlice ('nits'). You may see them on your tot's hair close to the scalp. Your pharmacist or health visitor can advise you on the best products to get rid of them.

* Regular combing with a 'bone comb' (a fine-tooth comb) at least twice a week will help to prevent any major head lice infestation.

* Supposedly preventive shampoos and sprays do not really prevent head lice.

LUNGS
* Never smoke in your child's presence and don't use aerosols or plug-in air fresheners as these may aggravate lung problems such as asthma.

* Ensure your little one gets plenty of fresh air.

* Check with your doctor or health visitor if your child develops wheezing, coughing (especially at night) or shortness of breath, or complains of pain or tightness in the chest. These are all symptoms of asthma.

toe

TEETH

✳ Brush twice a day with a soft-bristled children's toothbrush. For children under two years of age use a smear and for older children use a pea-sized amount of 1,000ppm fluoride toothpaste.

✳ Don't rinse their mouth with water – just let them spit out toothpaste residue so they keep fluoride in their mouth.

✳ All NHS dental treatment in Scotland is free for children up to the age of 16. Contact your local health board for details of NHS dentists in your area.

✳ Let your child see all the family brushing their teeth.

✳ Supervise the brushing yourself until your child is at least seven.

✳ Replace toothbrushes frequently.

✳ Both you and your child should visit the dentist regularly.

EYES

✳ Avoid risk of irritation by never smoking around your child.

✳ Consult your health visitor or doctor if your tot seems to have problems with their sight.

✳ Clues include squinting or cross-eyes, closing or covering one eye, rubbing the eyes a lot or a family history of sight problems.

EARS

✳ The ears are self-cleaning. Never poke a cotton bud into them!

✳ Tugging or holding the ears can be a sign of ear infection.

✳ Contact your doctor if your child is irritable, in pain or has a discharge from their ear.

✳ An ear or hearing problem may cause speech and language difficulties.

'I don't feel well.'

Every toddler feels under the weather occasionally, although it's usually not serious. Here's how to keep them healthy – and get them through those poorly spells.

6 easy ways to stay well

✳ Keep floors clean, and regularly change and wash bedding, clothes, towels and soft toys. Watch for any build-up of moulds or dust mites that can trigger allergies such as asthma.

✳ Keep kitchen surfaces clean and don't let pets go near family food. Always keep separate chopping boards for meat/poultry and vegetables/bread.

✳ Keep your home tidy to help avoid accidents (see also pages 52–53).

✳ Make sure your toddler washes their hands after going to the toilet. Do the same yourself, and also after changing their nappy or blowing your nose.

✳ Never smoke and don't let others smoke near your child, both indoors and in the car.

✳ Make sure your child gets all their immunisations (see page 54) and has the recommended check-ups.

Toddlers tend to get more minor illnesses such as coughs and colds than older children and adults do because their immune systems are still developing. So the occasional bout of illness is to be expected. It can also help them to build up immunity. But too many can wear them (and you) down. Healthy nutritious food, regular activity, fresh air and a few simple hygiene measures can help to keep them healthy and will prevent many common illnesses.

IS MY CHILD SICK?

You're the best judge of whether your tot is unwell, so if you think they're ill, even if you can't quite put your finger on what's wrong, don't hesitate to seek medical advice.

A classic sign of illness is a fever. Your child may have one if they're flushed or feel hot and sweaty, or if their temperature is over 38°C or 100.4°F measured with a thermometer. You can use a strip-type thermometer or a digital, non-breakable one; you can also get a rough idea by feeling their forehead.

Other clues that your child is under the weather include a runny nose, coughs and sneezes, a rash, sleeping more, lack of appetite, increased whining, clinginess and listlessness. If your tot's temperature doesn't stop them from playing and eating normally, there may not be anything to get too worried about.

Remember, if you are concerned, no matter what their temperature, call your health visitor or doctor. And, of course, you can call NHS 24 (see below) for free, confidential information and advice if your doctor's surgery is closed. This service will always find a doctor for you if required or contact the hospital.
■ NHS 24:
08454 24 24 24

IF YOUR TOT HAS A TEMPERATURE

✳ Encourage them to rest and drink plenty of fluids.

✳ They don't have to stay in bed unless they want to. It's OK for them to be with you as long as they can rest.

✳ Avoid exciting games and toys. Do quiet things with them until they feel better.

✳ Keep the room cool – open a window if it's hot.

✳ Dress them in just a nappy, or pants if they're toilet trained.

✳ If they're staying in bed, take the duvet or blanket off if they start sweating.

✳ Give sugar-free paracetamol syrup or ibuprofen for children. Always stick to the dose that's recommended. Remember, never give aspirin to a child under 16.

CARING FOR AN ILL CHILD

Kids are usually tired and grouchy when they are ill, so be patient and expect them to be more demanding. They may want to sleep more, so let them stay in bed if they ask. They'll probably want you around, so be prepared to spend time reading and watching TV together.

Keep things familiar and low-key – now is not the time to wean them off their dummy or change routines. If they're hungry, give them something light to eat and give them plenty to drink (drinking is more important than eating when they're ill). Once they're feeling better, they can go outside if the weather is fine but keep them indoors if it's cold, damp or foggy.

TOP TIP

You're the person most familiar with your toddler's health, so follow your instincts if you think there's something wrong that should be looked at by the doctor.

ALWAYS CALL THE DOCTOR OR NHS 24 OUT OF HOURS IF YOUR CHILD:

✳ cries constantly and can't be comforted
✳ seems drowsy and won't wake up
✳ has a fever that lasts for more than three days
✳ doesn't seem to be getting better after an operation or after a course of treatment for an illness.

Stay alert

Don't hesitate to see the GP if you're worried about the symptoms described below.

EXPERIENCED PARENTS

FIRST-TIME PARENTS

NEW HAND The dummy can be comforting for a new baby, but future problems can be avoided by controlling its use from the start.

OLD HAND One child may cheerfully give up the dummy but for a sibling it can become an obsession, and you'll have to wean them off it.

FITS AND FEVERS

A sharp increase in temperature can cause a febrile convulsion, or fit. The child goes stiff, loses consciousness, throws their head back and their limbs jerk. They go pale and may foam at the mouth. The attack ends after a few minutes, and the child returns to normal colour and consciousness or falls into a deep sleep. Up to one in 20 children aged one to four are affected. These fits are scary to watch but usually harmless.

Here's what to do

✳ Put them into the recovery position (pictured), lying on their side.
✳ Loosen clothing but don't try to hold them down.
✳ Don't put anything into their mouth, and remove anything they might swallow.

Always seek medical help

✳ After the first convulsion.
✳ If there's no improvement after a convulsion.
✳ If a convulsion lasts longer than five minutes.
✳ In case of breathing difficulties.
✳ If another one starts soon after the first.
Always report a convulsion to your GP.

MENINGITIS: EARLY SIGNS

The word meningitis strikes terror into any parent. You may be aware of classic warning signs such as:
✳ headache
✳ stiff neck
✳ sensitivity to light
✳ a pin-prick or purple blotchy rash that doesn't fade if you press on it with a glass.

But did you know that there are other signs of meningitis? These include:
✳ cold hands and feet
✳ mottled skin colour
✳ leg pain.

Research shows that these often appear much earlier than the classic signs so don't delay getting advice if your child has them – contact your doctor immediately.

PREVENTION: HOW TO WASH HANDS PROPERLY

Washing a toddler's hands will help protect them from stomach bugs and other illnesses.

✳ Wash hands before they eat, after going to the toilet or after playing with pets.

✳ Let them watch you washing your hands. Tots like to copy what you do.

✳ Show them how to wash their hands and in between their fingers, using soap and water.

✳ Help them by lifting them up to the basin or use a handy step-up stool.

✳ Make it fun by singing a rhyme or song.

PREVENTION: HOW TO LIMIT THE USE OF THE DUMMY

The dummy may have been a comfort to your tot when they were a baby, but prolonged use by toddlers can cause problems. Here are some tips on how to get rid of it – painlessly.

✳ Cut down use of the dummy by limiting it to certain times, such as bedtime or if they're ill.

✳ Use a distraction to divert their attention if they ask for it.

✳ Praise your toddler for not using the dummy.

✳ Point out other kids who don't use dummies.

✳ Stay calm and ignore any protests. They will grow out of using their dummy eventually.

✳ Be brave – throw it away! If you don't have a dummy in the house, you won't be tempted to give in when any protests become too loud.

Special delivery

If your child has specialised health needs, you'll need all your physical and emotional energies. The good news is you don't have to go it alone.

7 important questions

* ✳ What is the name of my child's condition?

* ✳ How can it be treated or managed?

* ✳ What extra support will my child need and who will provide this?

* ✳ How long will I have to wait to get the services my child needs?

* ✳ Where can I get more information about my child's problem?

* ✳ Are there any support groups or charities that can help my child, me or my other children?

* ✳ Could you put me in touch with any other parents of children with the same problem?

This may be the first of many assessments over the years. Rest assured that the team will aim to involve you closely in all decisions about your child's care.

In cases of chronic illness, disability or developmental, behavioural or emotional difficulties, there are services to support you and your child. Doctors, occupational therapists, speech and language therapists, physiotherapists, eye and hearing specialists, dietitians, psychologists and nurses are there and ready to help.

Tapping into the system

Your tot may have been identified as needing specialised care at birth or at an early-years check. But it may be you who notices something is not quite right. Be persistent until your concerns are properly addressed.

Your first port of call should be your health visitor or GP. They may refer you to a hospital specialist or to a child development centre, where you'll be able to see a community paediatrician and a team of other experts. Your child should be assessed quite quickly but the time it then takes to access the specialised services your child needs may vary considerably.

TOP TIP Having additional needs does not necessarily exclude your toddler from the things other children get involved in, such as parent and toddler groups or nursery. Many areas offer extra support to ensure all children are included.

EXPERT FILES
Consultant paediatrician
'Parents often say they had to fight to get a problem recognised or the services they need. Be prepared to persevere and demand what you feel your child needs.'
Dr Haider Mamdani, Child Development Centre, The Vale of Leven Hospital

Safety first

Boisterous, inquisitive toddlers can move like lightning, so you can't turn your back on them for a second. Our guide to safety around the home can help prevent nasty accidents.

Toddlers' natural curiosity and their growing physical skills, together with their lack of judgment, put them more at risk of accidents than when they were babies. You'll need to stay one step ahead at all times to ensure your home is safe. Think about the safety of other homes your tot spends time in too.

KITCHEN
It's best to keep little ones out of the kitchen altogether, except under strict supervision.

✳ Keep chemicals, medicines and cleaning products above child height. By 13 months, they can open containers.

✳ Fit short power leads on kettles and other appliances.

✳ Use the back burners of the cooker and turn pan handles away from the edge.

✳ Keep a fire extinguisher handy.

✳ Don't put chairs near the cooker as children can climb up.

✳ Always unplug the iron and put it safely out of reach while it cools.

✳ Keep hot drinks well away from little hands and don't reach over your tot's head to get a hot drink.

✳ If you have to leave the room, remove pans from the heat.

HALL AND STAIRS
✳ Fit a child safety gate at both top and bottom. You can also fit one to keep toddlers out of rooms such as the kitchen.

✳ Avoid accidents by keeping these areas well lit and free from toys and clutter.

✳ Make sure banisters are firmly fixed and steady all the way up.

✳ Check that stair carpets are fitted securely.

✳ Always hold on to the banister when carrying your tot upstairs.

✳ Never leave the front door open – your toddler can be through it and out on to the road in an instant.

LIVING ROOM
✳ This is where your little one is likely to spend most of their time, so be especially careful.

✳ Make sure electrical sockets are covered (use a dummy plug when not in use) and leads are well tucked out of the way.

✳ Check that appliances are in good working order and don't have cracked plugs or worn cables.

✳ Keep matches and lighters well out of reach.

✳ Keep sewing kits, scissors and knitting needles locked away.

✳ Cover any fires with a fireguard, preferably attached to the wall.

✳ Keep curtains away from fires.

✳ Don't leave alcoholic drinks or medicines where your toddler can get at them, and keep hot drinks out of reach.

✳ Make sure glass doors are made from shatterproof glass or add a safety film to the glass. (It can be bought from a baby shop).

✳ Put everything breakable or dangerous out of toddler reach.

TOP TIP

Fit smoke detectors on every floor of your home and change the batteries once a year. Have a plan in the event of a fire and make sure all your family know what to do if there is one.

❋ Keep cosmetics, razors, medicines and cleaning products locked in a high-level cabinet.

❋ Always take old medicines back to the pharmacy for safe disposal.

OUTSIDE
❋ Make sure all fences and gates are secure.

❋ Ensure there aren't any gaps in a fence or balcony slats that your child could squeeze through.

❋ Put a fence around a pond or pool, or fill it in. Always supervise kids near water.

❋ Keep kids out of the way when you're gardening or doing DIY in the house or garden.

❋ Site bonfires and barbecues away from fences, sheds and trees and supervise kids at all times.

❋ Lock away tools and chemicals.

❋ Teach your tot not to put berries or plants in their mouth.

IN THE CAR
❋ The law changed in September 2006 and now you must ensure that all children are secured in an appropriate car seat. See www.childcarseats.org.uk for further information.

OUT AND ABOUT
Always make sure your child is:

❋ in an appropriate car safety seat

❋ safely strapped into a five-point harness in their pushchair

❋ wearing a harness when walking

❋ reminded often about road safety and the dangers of traffic.

❋ Don't leave cigarette ends in ashtrays.

❋ Clean up all spills straight away.

❋ Store away rugs that they could trip over.

❋ Make sure everything breakable or dangerous is out of toddler reach.

BATHROOM
❋ Run cold water first and test the temperature of the bath before putting your child in.

❋ Reduce the hot water setting on your boiler thermostat.

❋ Use containers that have child-resistant tops.

❋ Never leave your child unattended in the bathroom.

❋ Cover hot towel rails with a towel to protect children.

❋ Never take electrical appliances into the bathroom.

EXPERT FILES
Consultant paediatrician

'Accidents in the home are a common reason for hospital admission in the toddler years, so have a checklist and make sure your home is safe every few weeks or months and at each new stage of your child's development. Your health visitor can help.'

Dr Zoë Dunhill, Edinburgh Sick Children's Hospital

Your health service

Once your child reaches the toddler stage, you probably won't see so much of your health visitor but you don't have to struggle on your own – there is still professional help and advice when you need it.

Your health visitor is still at the end of a phone, even when your child gets older. They probably left their number when you first saw them or it'll be in your child's red book, if you have one. The best time to call is first thing in the morning or towards the end of the working day. They will usually have an answering machine, so leave a message if they're not in.

Weekly baby clinics are often held in the GP surgery and are a good way of reaching your health visiting team. You can also contact them through local parent and child groups, nurseries and children's centres.

Make the most of your GP

Your GP is there to help you if your child is ill or if they have a chronic condition such as eczema or asthma.

Don't forget to take your child's red book and be ready to answer the following questions:
* How long has your child been ill?
* What are the symptoms – rash, coughing, diarrhoea?
* If there is a rash, where is it and is it itchy?
* Has your child been in contact with anyone with a similar illness?

You won't always come away with a prescription. Many illnesses get better on their own and overuse of antibiotics can lead to them being less effective.

Check it out

There are two routine immunisation and health check-ups during the toddler years. You will be told if the doctor or health visitor thinks your child needs any more.

HEALTH CONTACTS

AGE: 12 TO 13 MONTHS

WHAT FOR:

* Booster against Hib/Men C (Haemophilus influenzae type b (Hib) and meningococcal C (Men C) infections) around 12 months.

* MMR (mumps, measles and rubella vaccination) around 13 months.

* PCV (pneumococcal infection).

* Weighing.

* To observe how they walk if they are already on their feet.

* To discuss how you can keep your child healthy.

* To answer concerns about your child's development, health or wellbeing.

* To review your family's circumstances and needs.

YOU MIGHT WANT TO ASK:

* Can I expect any side effects from this vaccination and if so what can I do to ease them?

* Is my child walking properly?

* Can you explain the weight chart? Is my child the expected weight for their height and age?

* Do you think my child is developing normally?

* Are there any local support groups, networks or contacts that would be useful for me?

* When do you next want to see my child?

* Plus any questions you may have about food and nutrition, safety, looking after their teeth or anything else you're worried about.

AGE: 3 TO 5 YEARS

WHAT FOR:

* MMR vaccination.

* Booster against diptheria, tetanus, whooping cough (pertussis) and polio (DTaP/IPV).

* Weighing.

* To discuss how you can keep your child healthy.

* To answer any concerns you may have about your child's health.

* To review your family's individual circumstances and particular needs.

Most parents need a bit of extra help from time to time and in this section you'll find an A-Z list of useful organisations. They may have the answer – whether your child has an illness or chronic condition for which you need support and information, or whether you just want to know where to go for advice on different aspects of parenting.

*a-z ...find out more

WHAT YOU CAN FIND IN THIS SECTION — A TO Z

Helping hands

The following organisations can provide information and guidance on a range of childhood issues.

A

ACTIVITIES FOR TODDLERS
Tumble Tots (UK) Ltd
☎ 0121 585 7003
Bluebird Park
Bromsgrove Road
Hunnington, Halesowen
West Midlands B62 0TT
www.tumbletots.com

ASTHMA
Asthma UK Scotland
☎ 0131 226 2544
4 Queen Street
Edinburgh EH2 1JE
www.asthma.org.uk

AUTISM
The Scottish Society for Autism
☎ 0125 972 0044
Head Office
Hilton House
Alloa Business Centre
The Whins
Alloa FK10 3SA
www.autism-inscotland. org.uk

B

BEHAVIOURAL DIFFICULTIES AND ADHD
AFASIC (Children with Speech, Language and Communication Impairment)
☎ 0845 355 5577
50-52 Great Sutton Street
London EC1V 0DJ
www.afasic.org.uk

Hyperactive Children's Support Group
☎ 0124 353 9966
71 Whyke Lane
Chichester
West Sussex PO19 7PD
www.hacsg.org.uk

National Attention Deficit Disorder Information and Support Service
☎ 020 8906 9068
The ADDISS Resource Centre
10 Station Road
London NW7 2JU
www.addiss.co.uk

BENEFITS
www.direct.gov.uk/ Parents/YourMoney

C

CANCER AND LEUKEMIA
CLIC Sargent
☎ 0131 446 3456
5 Beaufort Road,
Edinburgh EH9 1AG

☎ 0141 572 5700
Mercantile Chambers
53 Bothwell Street
Glasgow G2 6TS
www.clicsargent.org.uk

CEREBRAL PALSY
Bobath Scotland
☎ 0141 435 3270
Bobath Scotland
Golden Jubilee National Hospital
Beardmore Street
Glasgow G81 4HX
www.bobathscotland. org.uk

Capability Scotland
☎ 0131 313 5510
ASCS (Advice Service Capability Scotland)
11 Ellersly Road
Edinburgh EH12 6HY
www.capabilityscotland. org.uk

Scope
☎ 0808 800 3333
6 Market Road
London N7 9PW
www.scope.org.uk

CHILDREN'S CENTRES/ DAY CARE
4Children
☎ 020 7512 2112
City Reach
5 Greenwich View Place
London E14 9NN
www.4children.org.uk

Daycare Trust
☎ 020 7840 3350
21 St George's Road
London SE1 6ES
www.daycaretrust.org.uk

National Day Nurseries Association
☎ 0870 774 4244
Oak House
Woodvale Road
Brighouse
West Yorkshire HD6 4AB
www.ndna.org.uk

Scottish Childminding Association
☎ 0178 644 9063
7 Melville Terrace
Stirling FK8 2ND
www.childminding.org

Scottish Pre-school Play Association
☎ 0141 221 4148
SPPA Centre
45 Finnieston Street
Glasgow G3 8JU
www.sppa.org.uk

CLEFT PALATE

Cleft Lip and Palate Association (CLAPA)
☎ 020 7833 4883
Green Man Tower
332B Goswell Road
London EC1V 7LQ
www.clapa.com

CROHN'S DISEASE / ULCERATIVE COLITIS

Crohn's in Childhood Research Association (CICRA)
☎ 020 8949 6209
Parkgate House
356 West Barnes Lane
Motspur Park
Surrey KT3 6NB
www.cicra.org

CYSTIC FIBROSIS

Cystic Fibrosis Trust
☎ 0845 859 1000
11 London Road
Bromley
Kent BR1 1BY
www.cftrust.org.uk

D

DEAF/HARD OF HEARING

National Deaf Children's Society Scotland
☎ 0808 800 8880
187-189 Central Chambers
93 Hope Street
Glasgow G2 6LD
www.ndcs.org.uk

DENTAL HEALTH

British Dental Health Foundation
☎ 0845 063 1188
Smile House
2 East Union Street
Rugby
Warwickshire CV22 6AJ
www.dentalhealth.org.uk

Childsmile Dental Health Programme
www.child-smile.org

DISABILITY SUPPORT

Contact a Family Scotland
☎ 0131 475 2608
Norton Park
57 Albion Road
Edinburgh EH7 5QY
www.cafamily.org.uk/ scotland

Disability Rights Commission Scotland
☎ 0845 762 2633
Freepost MID02164
Stratford-upon-Avon
CV37 9BR
www.drc.org.uk/scotland

The Family Fund
☎ 0845 130 4542
Unit 4
Alpha Court
Monks Cross Drive
Huntington
York YO32 9WN
www.familyfundtrust. org.uk

DOMESTIC VIOLENCE
Scottish Women's Aid
Scotland Domestic Abuse
☎ 0800 027 1234
132 Rose Street
Edinburgh EH2 3JD
**www.scottishwomensaid.
co.uk**

DOWN'S SYNDROME
Down's Syndrome Scotland
☎ 0131 313 4225
158/160 Balgreen Road
Edinburgh EH11 3AU
www.dsscotland.org.uk

DRUG AND ALCOHOL PROBLEMS
Alcohol Concern
☎ 0800 917 8282
Waterbridge House
32-36 Loman Street
London SE1 0EE
**www.alcoholconcern.
org.uk**

FRANK
☎ 0800 776 600
www.talktofrank.com

E

E.COLI
H.U.S.H
☎ 0800 731 4679
PO Box 159
Hayes UB4 8XE
www.ecoli-uk.com

ECZEMA/SKIN CONDITIONS
National Eczema Society
☎ 0870 241 3604
Hill House
Highgate Hill
London N19 5NA
www.eczema.org

EDUCATION
Parents Centre
☎ 0870 000 2288
The Department of
Education and Skills
Public Enquiry Unit
Sanctuary Buildings
Great Smith Street
London SW1P 3BT
www.parentscentre.gov.uk

EPILEPSY
British Epilepsy Association
☎ 0808 800 5050
New Anstey House
Gate Way Drive
Leeds LS19 7XY
www.epilepsy.org.uk

Epilepsy Scotland
☎ 0808 800 2200
48 Govan Road
Glasgow G51 1JL
**www.epilepsyscotland.
org.uk**

F

FIRST AID
British Red Cross – Scotland
☎ 0141 891 4000
4 Nasmyth Place
Glasgow G52 4PR
www.redcross.org.uk

St John Ambulance
☎ 0870 010 4950
27 St John's Lane
London EC1M 4BU
www.sja.org.uk

FOOD/NUTRITION ADVICE
Allergy UK
☎ 0132 261 9898
3 White Oak Square
London Road
Swanley
Kent BR8 7AG
www.allergyuk.org

**Food Standards Agency,
Scotland**
☎ 0122 428 5100
St Magnus House
25 Guild Street
Aberdeen AB11 6NJ
**www.food.gov.uk/
scotland**

G

GROWTH
Child Growth Foundation
☎ 020 8995 0257
2 Mayfield Avenue
London W4 1PW
**www.childgrowth
foundation.org**

H

HEART PROBLEMS
British Heart Foundation
☎ 0845 070 8070
14 Fitzhardinge Street
London W1H 6DH
www.bhf.org.uk

Children's Heart Federation
☎ 6 0808 808 5000
52 Kennington Oval
London SE11 5SW
**www.childrens-heartfed.
org.uk**

**The Scottish Association
for Children with Heart
Disorders**
☎ 0131 447 2711
104 Comiston Road
Edinburgh EH10 5QL
www.younghearts.info

K

KIDNEY DISEASE / RENAL FAILURE
**UK National Kidney
Federation**
☎ 0845 601 0209
6 Stanley Street
Worksop S81 7HX
www.kidney.org.uk

L

LEARNING DIFFICULTIES
ENABLE
☎ 0141 226 4541
7 Buchanan Street
Glasgow G1 3HL
www.enable.org.uk

Mindroom
☎ 0131 653 6235
PO Box 13684
Musselburgh EH21 1YL
www.mindroom.org

LUNG DISEASE
British Lung Foundation
☎ 0845 850 5020
73–75 Goswell Road
London EC1V 7ER
www.lunguk.org

M

MENTAL HEALTH
Young Minds
☎ 020 7336 8445
48-50 St John Street
London EC1M 4DG
www.youngminds.org.uk

N

NHS 24
If you're ill when your
GP surgery is closed and
you feel it cannot wait
until it re-opens, you
can call NHS 24 on
☎ 08454 24 24 24
Your condition will be
assessed by a nurse.

P

PARENTING ADVICE
Childcare link
☎ 0800 096 0296
childcarelink.gov.uk

Directov
**www.direct.gov.uk/
Parents**

Parentline Plus
☎ 0808 800 2222
www.parentlineplus.org.uk

R

RELATIONSHIPS
**Relationships Scotland
Relationship Counselling,
Family Mediation and
Child Contact Centres**
☎ 0845 119 2020
18 York Place
Edinburgh EH1 3EP
**www.relationships-
scotland.org.uk**

S

SOCIAL SUPPORT FOR
PARENTS
HomeStart
☎ 0800 068 6368
2 Salisbury Road,
Leicester LE1 7QR
www.homestart.org.uk

SureStart
☎ 0870 000 2288
SureStart Unit
Department for Education
and Skills and Department
for Work and Pensions
Caxton House
Tothill Street
London SW1H 9NA
www.surestart.gov.uk

SICK CHILDREN
**Action for Sick Children
Scotland**
☎ 0131 553 6553
172 Leith Walk
Edinburgh EH6 5EA
www.ascscotland.org.uk

STOP SMOKING
ASH Scotland
☎ 0131 225 4725
8 Frederick Street
Edinburgh EH2 2HB
www.ashscotland.org.uk

T

TERMINAL CHILD ILLNESS
ACT
☎ 0117 922 1556
Orchard House
Orchard Lane
Bristol BS1 5DT
www.act.org.uk

Useful numbers:

TWINS AND MULTIPLE
BIRTHS
Tamba
☎ 0800 138 0509
2 The Willows
Gardner Road
Guildford GU1 4PG
www.tamba.org.uk